iQ
BOOK

Marcel Feenstra

Philip J. Carter

Christopher P. Harding

WARD LOCK

A Ward Lock Book

First published in the UK

1993 by Ward Lock

A Cassell imprint

Villiers House

41/47 Strand

London

WC2N 5JE

The following questions are reprinted from the 4 Star Puzzler
(GAMES Magazine, 810 Seventh Avenue, NY 10019) and are © 1982
PSC GAMES Limited Partnership: 8-1; 14-1 and 2; 24-5, 6 and 7; 62
example and 1; and 76.

Distributed in the United States by Sterling Publishing Co., Inc.
387 Park Avenue South, New York, NY 10016-8810

Distributed in Australia by Capricorn Link (Australia) Pty Ltd
P.O. Box 665, Lane Cove, NSW 2066

British Library Cataloguing-in-Publication Data

A catalogue record for this book is available from the British Library

ISBN 0-7063-7148-8

Design and typesetting Malca Schotten, illustrations Ruth Rudd

Printed and bound in Great Britain by Cox & Wyman Ltd, Reading

Contents

About the Authors

Marcel Feenstra was born in Rotterdam in 1961. A Senior Research Fellow of I.S.P.E. (International Society of Philosophical Enquiry) and a member of Prometheus and the Mega Society, he first studied literature and linguistics at the University of Utrecht, then computer science, before starting his own computer consultancy, HiQ Systems, in 1987. He is currently a graduate student at the Fletcher School of Law and Diplomacy in Medford, Massachusetts.

Philip Carter was born in Huddersfield, West Yorkshire, in 1944, and he is an engineering estimator and lay magistrate. He is the author of several books, including the Take the IQ Challenge series, and is editor of the newsletter of the British Mensa Special Interest Group *Enigmasig*.

Chris Harding was born in the UK in 1944 but now lives in Australia. He is a member of several High-IQ societies, including Mensa, Intertel, Mega and Omega. He was the founder of I.S.P.E. and is a member of the International Test Commission, which polices IQ test standards throughout the world. He has been listed in the *Guinness Book of Records* under 'Highest IQ'. Among his awards are life membership of Intertel and Biography of the Year award from Historical Preservations of America.

Acknowledgements

Thanks are due to every one of the High-IQ society members who submitted material for use in this book. We have been delighted with the response, which made our final choice very difficult. Thanks also to all the High-IQ societies who ran our notice appealing for material in their journals. Our thanks to Jonathan Grimwood for recognizing that the idea of a book of puzzles and tests by High-IQ society members worldwide was one deserving of publication. Finally, our thanks to all our respective family members for their assistance with the project and words of encouragement.

Introduction

It was Marcel Feenstra who first suggested to Chris Harding the idea for a book of original puzzles and tests compiled by members of High-IQ societies. The fact that Marcel and Chris live on opposite sides of the globe, in Rotterdam and Queensland, might at first seem unusual for such a joint undertaking. However, High-IQ societies are international organizations, and they do not have the usual restrictions of boundaries and culture. Members are recruited on one criterion only: that of achieving a score on a supervised IQ test which puts the applicant in the top 2 per cent, or, in the case of some societies, the top 1 per cent or higher, of the population.

Basically, High-IQ societies are social clubs that encourage contact between members through meetings, dinners, lectures, conferences or correspondence. No one member, or group of members, has the right to speak or express opinions on behalf of the society. Because they are recruited on just the one criterion, all members are of equal standing. The largest and best known High-IQ society is Mensa, which accepts anyone for membership who has achieved a score within the top 2 per cent of the population on a supervised IQ test. 'Mensa' is the Latin word for 'table', thus suggesting a round table society. Other High-IQ societies, for example Intertel, have a qualifying level within the top 1 per cent of the population, while some are even more selective. The Mega society, for example, has its threshold at the 99.9999th percentile and accepts only one person in 1,000,000.

In this book we introduce you to just one of the many activities within the world of High-IQ societies: that of compiling and solving puzzles. We have put together a selection of puzzles and tests compiled by High-IQ society members worldwide which we are sure you will find both entertaining and challenging, and thought-provoking. As might be expected, the puzzles are of greatly varying degrees of difficulty. To enable you to monitor your performance throughout, we have allocated the following star rating system:

☆ Standard
☆☆ More challenging
☆☆☆ Difficult
☆☆☆☆ Very difficult
☆☆☆☆☆ Fiendishly difficult

For any puzzle that you are unable to crack, you will find that the answers section provides a clear explanation of what you should have done to come up with the correct solution. Each puzzle has been cross-referenced with two numbers – a question number (Q) and an answer number (A). This has enabled us to mix up the answers section so that there is no risk of seeing the answer before you tackle the next puzzle. We also include a separate section of so far unsolved puzzles and, finally, a compilation of IQ tests to enable you to assess your performance on three different types of test.

It has been a great pleasure and privilege to become involved in this book with Chris and Marcel, to select puzzles for inclusion from the many that we have received and to forge new friendships. We have set out to entertain and intrigue you and hope that you will spend many enjoyable hours working on the puzzles and tests which we have selected for you.

Good luck, and happy solving, and have fun!

Philip J. Carter

PUZZLES

ALPHABET CROSSWORD 1

AUDREY AUSTIN, AUSTRALIA

Using all 26 letters of the alphabet, once each only, fill in the blanks to complete the crossword with good English words.

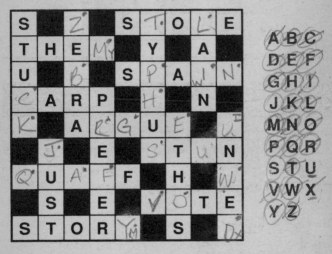

DOMINOES

DOUG PATTINSON, UK

Arrange the tiles in pairs within the grid to represent a complete standard set of 28 dominoes. There are four possible solutions because two pairs can be arranged in slightly different ways.

5	1	0	3	3	6	4	5
4	5	6	0	4	2	3	5
4	1	5	0	3	5	4	6
6	2	2	5	0	2	6	5
6	2	3	6	3	0	3	1
1	6	2	1	0	1	1	4
0	4	0	2	3	2	1	4

Q3   ☆   **A6**

LOGICAL PROGRESSION

ANTONIO CASAO IBAÑEZ, SPAIN

The following words are a logical progression:

Philosophicosociologically *26*
26 Zoo   *3*
3 Chronogrammatical
Quote
Entertained
Kiss
Disentanglement
Occultism *(I)*

Which of the following words should come next?

Scalp, Tawdry, Incest, Valetudinarianism

MAGIC SQUARES

J. CANTARA, FRANCE

In each square fill in the remaining numbers between 1 and 25 to form two different 5 x 5 magic squares in which each horizontal, vertical and corner-to-corner line totals 65.

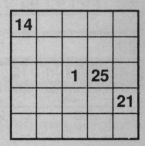

THREESOMES

ANDREW CHALLIS, UK

From the 30 three-letter words listed below, find 10 nine-letter words by putting three of the listed words together. For example, OFF + ICE + RED = OFFICERED.

DID	FAT	ION	WAR	INN	AGE
PER	BAY	RAN	THE	DEN	ATE
SPA	ADO	TEE	TIS	FUR	HER
OVA	GOD	TED	RAT	NEW	RED
PAR	TRY	ONE	CAN	TOR	SON

REVERSE LOGIC

CHRIS BEDFORD, UK

Which of the shapes below – A, B, C or D – comes next in this series?

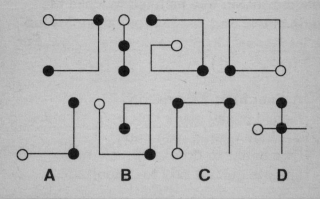

A **B** **C** **D**

ALPHAMETICS

MARCEL FEENSTRA, THE NETHERLANDS

In the following puzzle, the letters represent different digits. Substitute a digit for every letter to make this a valid addition. There are three known solutions, two of which are related.

```
  S O L V E
  T E S T S +
-----------
  G E N I U S
```

TRANSPOSALS

MITZI CHRISTIANSEN KUEHL, USA

A transposal is a word whose letters can be re-arranged to make new words - the letters of the word NAME can be used to make the words MANE and AMEN, for instance. Find the transposals in the verses that follow. For example:

> A diner from Kalamazoo
> Fished pesky black xxxx from his stew.
> Said the waiter, with cool,
> 'The better to drool.
> Imparts quite a xxxx to it, too!'

Answer: gnat, tang

1. I laughed about the castle ghost.
    'There's no such thing!' I said.
    But late that night a xxxxxxx seemed
    To hover near my bed.
    His xxxxxxx gleamed with ghostly gems,
    His crown with golden glow.
    He stirred in me a deep xxxxxxx -
    I guess my doubts must go.

2. A xxxxxx shower is due tonight,
   The weatherman said to take note.
   But since I can't even stay up till nine
   The chances are really xxxxxx.

3. There once was a champion jumping frog
   Who hated celebrity chores.
   Escaping his owner one fateful day,
   He bounded away out of doors.

   Alas, this poor creature, a naïve abroad,
   Jumped blissfully down a deep xxxxx.
   From zenith to xxxxx this xxxxx plunged,
   All creaking and flailing in vain.

4. The doc was poor and single
   Till he found a pretty bride.
   He then put up his xxxxxxx
   In the Xxxxxxx countryside.

5. The madam was very uncouth:
   While drinking a quart of vermouth
   She lost all of her glamour
   And got put in the slammer
   For trying to xxxxxx a xxxxxx.

6. Caught speeding at a dizzy yyyy
   While swigging from the distillate!
   Now, there's a xxxxxx to avoid.
   But who, you ask, was so devoid
   To mess up on the Interstate?
   A fine, upstanding xxxxxxyyyy!

7. Her 'great xxxxxx' misses dates
   And yo-yo like, he vacillates.
   He comes to see her when he can;
   He is, in truth, a xxxxxxx man.

8. Once, to *xxx*xx his great hunger, * stray
   Snatched * fat x*xx*xx mid much disarray.
   The butcher ran after
   Mid great gales of laughter.
   Wily old Fido, I xxxxx, got away.

9. Xxxxxxx, with its Halloween,
   Appeals to every child.
   There's something in its merriment
   That sets the spirit wild.

   When bats and cats and ghouls and rats
   And witches in their flight
   Yyy zealously xxyyyxxxyxx
   To make y scary night.

10. Behold the civilized house xxx
    Who, as a yyyy, won't harm a gnat -
    A friendly fluff of velveteen.
    But come the witching Halloween,
    Then by some law immutable
    His zzzz becomes zzzxyyxxzyy.

11. X yyyyyy zzz, and stillness reigns;
    The dying sun's horizon-low.
    Birds yyyyyyzxzz, like tiny chains,
    Their tracks upon the fallen snow.

12. The yyyyy surveyed the xxxxx and traps,
    The smorgasbord of tasty scraps;
    Remembered, though, what he'd been
        taught:
    Xxxxyyxyyy mice do not get caught.

13. The old xxxyyyzzzz down the street
    Who hated man and beast
    Brought home a stray one rainy day
    And fed him quite a feast.

    But then the xxx got in some yyy
    And tracked it everywhere:
    On spotless floor and costly rug
    And master's good armchair.

    Xxxyyyzzzz sorely disapproved.
    Oh, how he carried on!
    What happened to the sorry xxx?
    The next day he was zzzz!

In the next two transposals, which are more
difficult, each letter is represented by a
different number.

14. On chilly, dark October 123456,
    Strange 3789216, 347656 and fearsome
        623456
    Cavort abandoned in the streets,
    In full pursuit of tricks or treats.

15. A 123456, snowy Christmas day;
    Some merry singers come my way.
    I 321645, filled with reverie
    While hanging 625143 on my tree;
    Invite them, in 453216 their aid
    And ply them with hot lemonade.

In the final puzzle in this group the numbers represent two anagrammatical words. Each word has three syllables - and meter is everything!

16. Cook roasted a turkey with pride,
    Removed it and set it aside.
    Along came a stray,
    Dragged turkey away,
    123453678 633245178 outside.

ODD ONE OUT 1

TONY LAYTON, UK

Which of these is the odd one out?

- DERBY
- EDINBURGH
- ABERDEEN
- NEWCASTLE
- LIVERPOOL
- SALISBURY

MATCH PLAY 1

MARCEL FEENSTRA, THE NETHERLANDS

The following statement is not true at present. Move one match only to make it true.

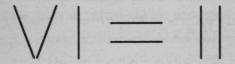

We have produced four possible solutions to this puzzle. How many can you find?

Q11	☆☆	A34

WORDS

LLOYD KING, UK

Find the next most appropriate word.

Think
Tsar
Knot
Hallway
Swat
They
?

Choose from: Seam, Pyramid, Time, Stone, Enigma, Run

CRYPTIC WORD SQUARE 1

AUDREY AUSTIN, AUSTRALIA

A 6 x 6 magic word square is one in which the same six words read the same both across and down. The answer to each of the six cryptic clues are all six-letter words, which form a magic 6 x 6 word square.

	1	2	3	4	5	6
1						
2						
3						
4						
5						
6						

Clues

1. Dispel misspelt and badly pronounced as well.
2. I alter poems. It's all put on!
3. Separate in South Africa and part of Ancient Greece.
4. An entrance to the harbour?
5. A broken teaset for the station.
6. Businessman - who gives out the cards?

FATUITOUS PECULIARITY

JOHN B. ROCKWELL, USA

Apart from its fatuity, what is peculiar about the following sentence?

Odysseus sailed down narrow, winding gulfs, sounded deep pools, savoured delightful lasagna, and, defying God, drove eastward direct to Oporto.

ANAGRAMS 1

MITZI CHRISTIANSEN KUEHL, USA

An anagram is an apposite re-arrangement of a familiar phrase. For example, I AM A PENCIL DOT is an anagram of A DECIMAL POINT (1, 7, 5). The numbers indicate the number of letters in each word of the answer, and an asterisk after a number indicates a capitalized word.

1. DEFIANTLY RUIN TREE FARM (13*, 5, 3)
2. FLINCH WITH COLD RATE (3, 4, 5, 6)

THEOREM

DOUG PATTINSON, UK

The letter grid contains a hidden statement. Can you work out the logic and find the statement?

T	H	S	M	F	T	W	C
N	S		C	T	V	T	E
R	N	G	L	R	N	U	O
M		B	R	S	O		O
S		S	Q		E		U
	R	N	I		E	I	A
M	B	U		A	U		E
R	I	A	U	A	E	U	E

HOMOPHONES

TONY LAYTON, UK

A homophone is a word that is pronounced in the same way as another - for example, the words 'son' and 'sun' are homophones.

Find two homophones for each pair of clues below. The 24 answers on the left start with each letter of the alphabet with the exception of x and z, but their homophones on the right

do not necessarily start with the same letter.
The clue pairs are *not* in alphabetical order.

Cure: Spur
Fish: Looked
Ranks: Flower
Mould: Require
Long ago: Zigzag
Consumed: Island
Employ: Sheep
Bird: Junior
Grab: Regards
Bribe: Run
Born: Cry
Cellar: Gait
Keep in view: Indeed

Pair: Also
Conserve: Post
Summon: View
Alternative: Wonder
Firework: Streak
Chaps: Behaviour
Trim: Fruit
Wharf: Island
Moisture: Owed
Ransack: Stringed
instrument
Wraps: Gorse

CRYPTOGRAM 1

MITZI CHRISTIANSEN KUEHL, USA

This cryptogram is a straight substitution code
in which each letter of the alphabet has been
replaced by another.

CIRCUITS BRZTSRY FIB CRCUAD LATSXY

FAR PFGHEUHY OREJRAY KORI IULOTIM
REYR YLTSXY.

GHL LORI, LU ARCRCGRA CIRCUITSY T PTIB,

LORD NFC HJ LOR STASHTLY UP CD
FBBERB CTIB.

REBUS AND SYMBOLS CROSSWORD

AUDREY AUSTIN, AUSTRALIA

A rebus is a riddle in which a word or phrase is represented by pictures or arrangements of letters. For example, YAW = backwardsway.

All the clues to this novel crossword are rebuses and symbols, with the exception of 8 down, which is an anagram to get you started.

Clues

Across

7. L
   S (6)
9. A 6 @ / S (8)
10. . (4)
11. $\rightarrow$ ✓ (5)
12. 568ml (4)
13. R (3)
14. EVAR (6)
15. V2 (4)
18. UU – (7)
19. P o (7)
22. + + (4)
23. Ɛ (6)
24. Y (3)
26. O (4)
28. 6 BES (5)
29. C LONG – N (4)
30. Sunday, Monday, Tuesday, Wednesday, Thursday, Friday, Saturday (5,3)
31. . ING (6)

Down

1. NON+ED (10)
2. △ (5)
3. (7)
4. Mr (6)
5. ś (9)
6. Fe (4)
8. Airless (Anagram) (7)
16. 10th o (5,5)
17. + 4 4 4 (4,5)
20. X ? (7)
21. Mix, Rogers, etc. (7)
23. ÷ (6)
25. / (5)
26. N V (4)

FOOTFALLS

DOUG PATTINSON, UK

A man and his smaller son set off walking side by side. Eleven footfalls later their feet touch the ground simultaneously for the first time. If the son's stride is 70cm, how long is the father's stride?   *770*

SQUAREWORD

ANDREW CHALLIS, UK

Place the words listed opposite into the grid so that each vertical and each horizontal line contains two three-letter words and one four-letter word in any order – i.e., 4-3-3, 3-4-3 or 3-3-4 – and so that no letter appears in any single line more than once. The first word has already been entered to get you started.

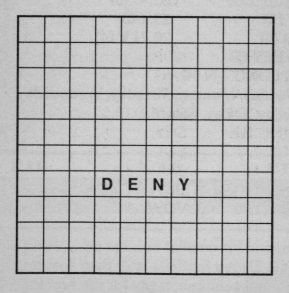

Across

CHOP	ALM	NEU
COLD	ARI	OFT
~~DENY~~	ASK	SHE
ENDS	BAN	SOU
EPIC	HOP	TRY
IDLY	ISH	UFO
OPAL	KGB	URE
SCAG	LEG	VIE
TYPE	MOA	WAR
WASH	MOP	WIT

Down

ASHY	ACT	KOP
BLOW	AMP	LUG
DEAR	CIA	NIP
DUPE	DOE	RAM
ECHO	DUB	SHY
HONK	FAR	SOL
ISLE	FIE	SPA
NERO	GYP	UCT
NEWT	HIS	VOW
OLEG	ITS	YAM

SEQUENCE

LLOYD KING, UK

What is the next word in this sequence?

Redden
Seam
Blew
Hatred
Dense
Amble
?

MANAGRA PARIS

TONY LAYTON, UK

Solve the following clues to get 28 words, then sort them out to get 14 anagram pairs. For example, 1. Thicken and 7. Kitchen.

1. Make more viscous
2. Authorize
3. A systematic account
4. Detective
5. People with defective mental development
6. Swindlers
7. Cooking department

8. Morning service
9. Absence of sound
10. Wishful thinker
11. Straightforward
12. Yews, pines, firs etc
13. Responded
14. Ensnare
15. Business
16. Reservoir
17. A record
18. A type of evidence
19. Guardian
20. Refurnish with a weapon
21. Esteem
22. Praying insect
23. Pitiless
24. Type of palm
25. Jostle
26. Military chevrons
27. Provided
28. Continue steadfastly

THE TWENTIETH-CENTURY BOGGLE

ANTONIO CASAO IBAÑEZ, SPAIN

In this 5 x 5 square all the years from 1901 to 1928 are written 'boggle' style – that is, to express any year you have to begin on a square and move to an adjacent square, horizontally, vertically or diagonally. You cannot use a square twice for the same year, but every square may be used as many times as you wish for different years.

The challenge is to place the largest number of consecutive years from 1901 onwards in a 5 x 5 square.

2	7	3	8	6
2	4	2	5	8
1	9	0	6	1
0	3	1	7	9
8	9	5	1	9

CHARADES

MITZI CHRISTIANSEN KUEHL, USA

In a charade two or more words in sequence make up a longer word – woo-den (wooden), for instance. Find the words in the following charades. For example:

Xxxx, xxxx Yyyy got the zzzz again.
Poor, poor, Will, whip
(Father, mad, failed to count to ten.)
Now, xxxx Yyyy in the nighttime chill
poor, Will
Sits and cries with the zzzzxxxxyyyy.
whippoorwill

1. A skinny, freckled kid xx yyy,
   Oh, how the boys disdained her then!
   Xx thirteen, with her awkward stance
   She hugged the wall xx every zzzzz.
   Xx seventeen, it's funny how
   Boys zzzzz xxyyyzzzzz on her now!

2. There was a xxxx of facile tongue,
   Of devastating, yyyxxxx wit.
   But not above a lowly yyy
   Whene'er occasion called for it.

3. Jack and Jill went up the hill
   xxyyyzzz
   Xx yyy a pail of water.
   Jill then slipped and took a spill.
   Xx yyy zzz,
   Jack ran down and caught zzz.

4. Though victim of an act so vile,
   The xxxyyyyyy xxx yyyyyy all the while.
   But once he woke and saw his plight
   He bit and kicked with all his might.
   The poachers viewed this with alarm
   And took the xxx back to the farm.

5.   Our yyyyyy left a cryptic note
      In xxxx of two months' rent;
      A young xxxxyyyyyy turned her head
      And off to France they went.

Beheadment

In a beheadment the first few letters of an initial word are systematically dropped – for example, cheat-heat-eat.

6.   You can hear the outboard zyxxxxx;
      You can see the speedboat stop.
      I have told you not to yxxxxx
      In old Wilson's backyard shop.

      You forgot to oil the rotors
      When you worked upon their boat.
      Now it's xxxxx chaos – boaters
      Drifting helplessly afloat.

Charade/Beheadment

In a charade two or more words make up a longer word. In the following puzzle, the first letter of the longest word is dropped.

7.   'Xxx sad, the tendency to yyy
      On slightest provocation,
      Though xxxyyy-thin the xxyyy be,
      Or false the allegation.

CROSSNUMBER

AUDREY AUSTIN, AUSTRALIA

1		2	3			4				5	6	7
8	9				10			11				
12			13	14			15					
16		17		18			19	20		21		
	22		23		24						25	26
27		28							29			
30	31			32		33		34				
35			36					37		38		
	39	40				41	42		43		44	
45				46	47			48		49		
50	51				52			53	54			
55				56			57					

In this 'all-number' crossword, several of the answers require general knowledge. The rest can be calculated.

Across

2. Spots on a set of dominoes
4. Pieces of silver
5. 18 across x 5
8. 10 down – 17 down – 4 down – 29 across – 2 down
10. A square
11. Factor of 33404
12. Days in a lunar month
13. Every digit is either 1 more or 1 less than the preceding digit
16. First digit is ⅔ total of the remaining 2 digits
18. Prime number
19. Anagram of 29 down
22. DCCXXVI
24. Sum of the first 2 digits = the sum of the remaining 2 digits
25. A card game
28. 56 across in reverse
29. Arithmetic progression
30. Different odd digits
34. A square
35. Total American States
36. Digits total solution of 10 across
37. 29 across x 2 + 34 across + 6 down
39. Digits total solution to 56 across
41. 4 across in reverse
43. Consecutive digits
46. 11 in binary
49. Digits total 6
50. 31 down x first 2 digits of 47 down
52. A deck minus the pictures
53. 36 across + 17 down
55. Digits total solution to 14 down
56. Prime number
57. 31 down in reverse

Down

1. A cube
2. 42 down in reverse
3. First digit is ⅔ sum of the remaining 2 digits
4. Degrees in a rectangle
5. Year George II of England was crowned
6. Which clue's answer is 3297?
7. Anagram of 27 down
9. Digits total 28
10. LUCKY Scrabble values
14. Movie Catch
15. Year Edward VIII was crowned and abdicated
17. Digits total 21
20. Knights of the Round Table
21. Third digit = sum of the first 2 digits
23. 10 across in reverse
26. A square
27. A quarter past two
29. A cube
31. Prime number
32. Year George I of England born
33. Pennsylvania number
34. Factor of 765
36. Third highest score with one dart
38. Four hours before noon
40. 53 across in reverse
42. A date in October: Hallowe'en
44. 10 down − 5 down
45. Palindrome
47. Digits total same as those of 37 across
48. Multiple of 4 across
51. First 2 digits of 7 down in reverse order
54. Second digit is ⅓ first digit

A SONNUNDRUM

K. C. COOPER, GERMANY

This is a rather tortured cross between a
sonnet and a puzzle – hence the awful name.
The idea is to use rhyme, meter and context to
fill in the blanks and then to establish the
common theme linking the missing words.

This is the story of Airman _____,
          who came from _____,
No _____ he, but a man to like,
          just like his old _____.

In his _____ he looked a treat, a star in the _____,
Though as a _____ hard to beat, for _____ he fell.

He encountered her last _____,
          by an _____ machine,
To become a male _____ for her,
          was his ev'ry _____ keen.

But _____ was a Casanova, ev'ry bit a _____,
Speaking a Mississippi _____-ese,
          drinking corn _____.

He pursued, like a _____ hunter, the _____ of Aqaba,
To a high _____, after her, northwest of old _____,

Our brave pilot, from _____, flew in,
          the _____, our hero,
With a _____ he did his girl win,
          his foe a mere _____.

At the wedding feast they danced a _____,
And the guests all shouted a loud _____.

ODD ONE OUT 2

TONY LAYTON, UK

Which of the following words is the odd one out?

RESET, LEMON, MANGO, BATCH, CADGE

DEVILLED FRUIT

BOB NEWMAN, UK

Recipe: for each clue, choose a word to split and insert the fruit of your choice. Re-arrange the spacing and punctuation to taste (although you may not alter the order of the letters) to give something that still makes sense – usually more sense than the original. For example: 'That fireplace is supposed to be as aid, my father' yields 'That fireplace is supposed to be Adam, son,' said my father – hence DAMSON. (These are known as printer's devilry clues.)

1. If you're thinking of moving into an old house, my advice is 'Look before you lease!'

2. In India they charge snakes with musical trickery.

3. By heading straight for Lowestoft beach, the robber made the coast.

4. The sow hoped to reach her hog before nightfall.

5. Whatever the regent does, make a profit.

6. I must pay off the loans – harsh interest rates were not always so high.

7. It was a wonderful Balt, a man from Riga, who wanted to take me home to Latvia.

8. Tweedledum said he'd hidden the rattle in the jar, said Tweedledee.

9. Rising from the mists in the eerie caverns, a frightful odour – attention!

10. Consider the effect of that McEnroe bravery – true American heart.

11. The hug to associate with bears is a strong and fearless one.

12. As I left the casino for my hotel room I was offered a dice; cup of cocoa was what I wanted.

13. Look at the goddess in the beautiful woollen cloak! Isn't that Hera?

14. Hog ate date ton as we boys grew weary of school food.

15. I know you're going to the disco, but do you have to wear those really heinous trousers?

16. After the moonshine, Panama hat hijack is less appealing.

17. You must remember the knife – very Arabian, you see – is to welcome you as a brother in Islam.

18. I'd heard so much about Alvaro Mendoza the football coach that while in Central America I simply had to visit the man – and Al's team.

19. Tonight on the South Bank Show we examine the work of Pablo Hernandez, an enigmatic playwright, an obscure novelist, a curt critic, and a major figure in the cultural life of his country.

20. The exact centre of our pub is to be determined by the official baiter.

NUMBERS

LLOYD KING, UK

What is the next number in this series?

27, 11, 6, 3, 5 ?

CRYPTIC WORD SQUARE 2

AUDREY AUSTIN, AUSTRALIA

A 6 x 6 magic word square is one in which the same six words read the same both across and down. The answers to each of the six cryptic clues are six-letter words, which form a magic 6 x 6 word square.

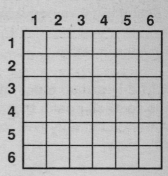

Clues
1. Could be this shy in the judge's chamber.
2. Assume otherwise entertains.
3. Wine or weapon for the listeners.
4. Bond prevents what movies provide.
5. There was a solitary one in famous painting.
6. A formidable countenance to the rear.

FRACTIONS

PETER SCHMIES, GERMANY

That $^{16}\!/_{64} = \frac{1}{4}$ can be demonstrated by cancelling both 6s. Can you find other fractions, excluding such trivial cases as $^{55}\!/_{55}$, with this property?

Q32 **A69**

FRAGMENTED QUOTATION

ANDREW CHALLIS, UK

Complete this well-known quotation (9 words – 2, 3, 3, 10, 2, 3, 13, 2 and 6 letters respectively – 44 in all) by inserting the 22 pairs of letters in their correct sequence.

$$\_\_ \ / \ \_\_\_ \ / \ \_\_\_ \ / \ _____ \ /$$
$$\_\_ \ / \ \_\_\_ \ / \ _____ \ /$$
$$/ \ \_\_ \ / \ _____$$

ED	OS	TE	AR	TI	OF	RE	EN	OT
FE	LI	DE	TH	WE	SI	ES	IN	ST
BI	AT	EP	IN

SQUARE AND SQUARE ALIKE

LLOYD KING, UK

In which one of the five boxes – A, B, C, D or E – can a dot be put so that it meets the same conditions as the one in the box on the left?

A   **B**   **C**   **D**   **E**

MEENY AND MOE

MEL BEBEE, USA

Meeny and Moe decide to play a game of dice. Meeny proposes rules as follows:

'Moe, you choose a number between one and six and throw three dice. If your number faces up, I pay you $1. If your number does not face up, you pay me $1. Since the odds of your number facing up on one die is 1-6, and since you use three dice, we have an even game.'

Moe, who always looks for an advantage, modifies the rules as follows: 'We will play according to the rules you have stated except that you must pay me $1 for *each* die on which my number is face up. If it shows twice I get $2. If it shows once I get $1. If it doesn't show face up at all, I pay you $1.'

Meeny reluctantly agrees. Is it now a fair game (50-50 probability)? If not, who has the advantage and how much?

THINKING MAN'S SERIES

BOB NEWMAN, UK

Who comes next in the series:

SOCRATES
SARTRE
PLATO
BOOLE
HEIN
ABBAS

Is it

AARON, KNOX, SPINOZA, BEDE OR RAMSEY?

VERBAL ANALOGY TEST

JOE DAVIES, UK

These analogy questions test knowledge as well as the ability to research information. There is no time limit, and any works of reference may be consulted. A performance rating is given with the answer.

1. MAN is to BINOCULAR as CYCLOPS is to ?

2. SAME is to DIFFERENT as HOMO- is to ?

3. GARMENTS is to TAILOR as CANDLES is to ?

4. BULL, MAN is to MINOTAUR as LION, GOAT, DRAGON is to ?

5. MERCURY is to LEAD as CINNABAR is to ?

6. NERVE is to NEURO as KIDNEY is to ?

7. RIVER is to WIND as ALLUVIAL is to ?

8. INVENTIVE is to DAEDALIAN as VIOLENTLY MAKING TO A STANDARD is to ?

9. MATHEMATICS is to DODGSON as WONDERLAND is to ?

10. NEW is to OLD as NEO- is to ?

11. COBWEB is to ARACHNOID as TREE is to ?

12. BLACK is to STYGIAN as FORGETFUL is to ?

CRYPTARITHM

MITZI CHRISTIANSEN KUEHL, USA

Each letter represents a digit and TRY is itself a square number.

$$TRY^2 = ANYHOW$$

EXTRAWORDS

ANDREW CHALLIS, UK

Hidden in each set of six three-letter words is a 15-letter word, which can be found by re-arranging the letters from five of the six three-letter words. The word you are looking for in each case will match the clue provided. The sixth word in each line is merely a red herring but the letters of the five unused words can be re-arranged to form the name of a county in the south of England - can you find it?

1. COD ALL YEN IRK RAY AIM
                        Designed for flight
2. HIM MEN HOP EAT ARC RIG
                        Film maker
3. RIP SHE HEM SON PIN SEA
                        Failure to understand
4. VIA GUN DOE SAD BUG SAT
                        Not beneficial
5. SUE CAN BIN SIR HEN LOG
                        Local sociability

SEEK WITH DIFFERENT BASES

ANTONIO CASAO IBAÑEZ, SPAIN

A four-digit decimal number, SEEK (in which the letters S, E and K each represent a different digit), is expressed in base 7, base 6 and base 5. Treating these three expressions of SEEK as decimal numbers, we add them together and find that the total is 54321. What is SEEK?

LETTER DELETION

MITZI CHRISTIANSEN KUEHL, USA

In letter deletion, one letter is deleted from the first word to form the second word.

1. The little tin xxxxyxx that broke in two
   Was patched up with xxxxxx as good
   as new.

2. A pox on camping out, I say!
   The 'xxyxxxxx' gear weighs a ton.
   The water isn't xxxxxxx,
   I'm burned to a crisp from the sun.

WORD SEARCH: SHAKESPEARE'S PLAYS

AUDREY AUSTIN, AUSTRALIA

The grid contains the names of 27 of the plays of William Shakespeare. They can be found reading up, down, across or diagonally backwards or forwards, but always in a straight line. Not all the letters are used.

```
T T A N G N I H T O N T U O B A O D A H C U M
T H E T W O G E N T L E M E N O F V E R O N A
O T E I H R C Y M B E L I N E L N E D G D M L
W R R M I E L A T S R E T N I W E H T R I E L
E O A O E A M K I N D A O P D E S O A D T A S
R I V N S R N E D A S T G I N T Z S S R H S W
H L E O R A R T R R A E L G N I K U Y A A U E
S U T F O T C Y O C O L M S G N M N O S U R L
E S T A R M H C W N H P R Q E M D A U E T E L
H A H T R I P G S I Y A U W E V R L L A E F T
T N E H E R E L I N V A N R Y E S O I C L O H
F D T E F O R L U N C E N T E D M I K S M R A
O C E N O S I P R D H I S D O A T R E U A M T
G R M S Y A C A P O G T T O C F E O I I H E E
N E P C D O L L E H T O F B F L V C T L E A N
I S E O E C E T T M I S E L C W E E D U D S D
M S S U M O S S I O L T B U E E I O N J A U S
A I T J O R D I N A H A R E S W S N P I Y R W
T D T N C R U N G A J I G A R A T T D A C E E
E A C H E L O V E S L A B O U R S L O S T E L
H D L A H I N X T E I L U J D N A O E M O R L
T O M A T P S U C I N O R D N A S U T I T R A
```

FARMER GILES'S FIELD

GEOFF HINCHLIFFE, UK

Farmer Giles's field will support 60 sheep for a maximum of 6 days, *or* 30 cows for a maximum of 3 days, *or* 20 sheep and 10 cows permanently. If Giles sells all his cows, how many sheep can he keep permanently in his field?

FIND THE LADY

BOB NEWMAN, UK

Discover what the following words have in common, then tell me who my darling is. You should also be able to find out how old she is, her star sign and the colour of her eyes. Finally, you can probably guess on which day of the week I first met her, and what meteorological phenomenon it felt like.

TURKEY
AFGHANISTAN
CHIMPANZEE
TUPPENCE
QUARTER
DOUBLE BASS (or double BALALAIKA)

SERIES

PETER SCHMIES, GERMANY

What is the next number in this series?

0, 1, 1, 1, 0, 1, 4, 1, 7, 5, 3, 1 ?

FIGURE IT OUT

LLOYD KING, UK

Which shape – A, B, C, Ɔ or E – comes next in this sequence?

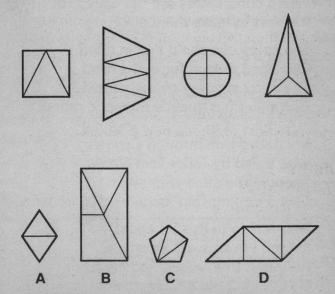

LETTER ADDITION

MITZI CHRISTIANSEN KUEHL, USA

In the following puzzles one letter has been added to a word when it is used a second time. For example: screen fame, screen frame.

1. She planned a dinner tête-à-tête
   To xxxxx yyyyyy with her boss.
   The lights were low, the music soft,
   But dinner proved a total loss.

   (A teaspoon's not a tablespoon,
   A whisper's not a shout.
   When condiments are not called for,
   It's best to leave them out.)

   The spicy eve she'd had in mind
   Occurred in fact; for in the food
   The xxxxx yzyyyyy overwhelmed,
   And killed her guest's romantic mood.

2. My naked ride through Coventry
   Was spied by Tailor Tom alone.
   Though punished with xxxxxxxx,
   This 'Peeping Tom' became well known.

   Xxxxyxxxx like this I'd shun!
   In fact, I think we'll all agree,
   Although this tailor's had his fun,
   He couldn't pin a thing on me.

3. Hillary, Mallory conquering
   Everest. (How in the world did they dare?)
   Coolly asserted, 'To xxx xx up,
   Everest's xxxxxx was temptingly there.'

WORD SEQUENCE

LLOYD KING, UK

What is the next word in this sequence?

Base
Minor
Upstart
Helicon
Curate
?

Choose from:
Tectonic, Iron, Meridian, House, Xenophobia

DIGITAL CLOCK

LLOYD KING, UK

At 16 minutes past two one afternoon a man, who does not known the time, consults his digital clock. It shows 2.17. How does he know it is incorrect?

ALPHABET CROSSWORD 2

AUDREY AUSTIN, AUSTRALIA

Using all 26 letters of the alphabet, once each only, fill in the blanks to complete the crossword with good English words.

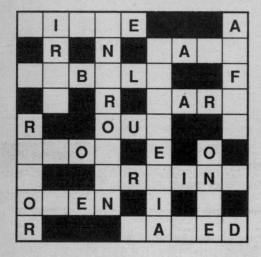

A B C
D E F
G H I
J K L
M N O
P Q R
S T U
V W X
Y Z

SEQUENCE

MARCEL FEENSTRA, THE NETHERLANDS

Which of the symbols – A, B, C, D or E – continues this sequence?

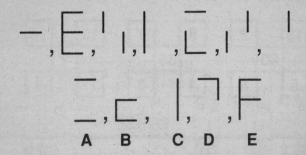

A B C D E

CODED MESSAGE

ANTONIO CASAO IBAÑEZ, SPAIN

Can you break the following code and find a quotation by the American comedy actor Jim Backus?

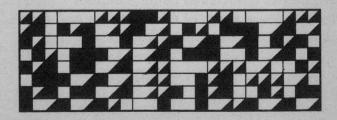

MISSING NUMBER

PETER SCHMIES, GERMANY

Study each set of numbers and then work out the missing number in the third set.

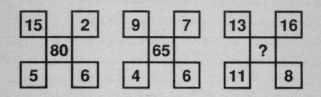

HIDDEN TREASURE

TONY LAYTON, UK

Find 26 ways (or more?) in which the friends could have paid for their meal.

An eagle pie meal at Reeth alerted a man named Levi and friends to realize how wonderful alternative cuisine tasted. 'I meant to bolt down a cob of rancid butter and a rich, milky farmhouse cheese for dessert, but Mark, Joey, Tom and Louise recommended grapes or turnip ice cream!'

THE COLLECTOR'S BEQUEST

PEARL CHIRPIT, UK

A rich collector of gold coins left a very complicated will giving instructions as to how his gold coin collection (of fewer than 5,000 coins) was to be distributed among his 10 children – five sons and five daughters – after his death. The instructions he gave were that first of all one gold coin was to be given to his butler, then exactly a fifth of those remaining had to go to his eldest son. Another coin was then given to the butler, then exactly a fifth of those still remaining went to his second eldest son. This procedure was then repeated exactly until all his five sons had received a share, and the butler had been given five golds coins. Then, after the fifth son had taken his share the gold coins still remaining were to be equally divided among his five daughters. How many gold coins did the collector have in his collection?

REBUSES

LLOYD KING, UK

A rebus is an arrangement of letters or symbols representing a word or phrase. Can you solve these 12 rebuses?

1 stuvw	2 pl**ot**	3	4 glibness
5 co ifer	6 o o o |o|	7 tsetaocrump	8 a e

9 000
     0
    0 0
     0
    000
	10 **10ŀ**	11 rdinary	12 , ,
			  , ,
			  , ,
			  , ,

STRAIGHT AND TRUE NUMBERS

ANTONIO CASAO IBAÑEZ, SPAIN

The numbers that can be written in capital letters made up of straight lines only – for instance, NINE – are called *straight* numbers. If the value is equal to the number of lines that comprise it, it is called *straight and true* or 'orthonymic'.

ELEVEN

Can you find any straight and true numbers in the English or any other language?

CONSONANT LOSS

AUDREY AUSTIN, AUSTRALIA

In this puzzle all the consonants have been omitted. Can you fill them in to reveal 26 occupations?

1. _ A _ _ E _
2. _ E _ I _ _
3. _ O _ E _
4. _ I _ E _ A _
5. _ O _ _ _ A _
6. _ U I _ _ E _
7. _ _ O U _ I E _
8. _ O O _ _ A _ E _
9. _ A _ I _ U _ I _ _
10. _ O U _ _ _ A _ I _ _
11. U _ _ O _ _ _ E _ E _
12. _ E A U _ I _ I A _
13. _ _ _ I _ _
14. _ O _ _ O _

---

15. _ U _ _ E	22. _ E _ E _ _ E _
16. _ A _ _ E _	23. A _ _ O U _ _ A _ _
17. _ O _ I _ E _ A _	24. _ _ I _ O _ _ A _ _ E _
18. _ E _ _ E _	(2 words)
19. _ A _ _ E _ _ E _	25. E _ _ I _ E E _
20. _ O _ E _ _	26. _ A I _ _ _ E _ _ E _
21. _ U _ _ _ I _ E _	
(2 words)	

Q58 ☆☆☆ **A37**

WORD BLOCK

ANDREW CHALLIS, UK

Rearrange the 12 12-letter words so that two more 12-letter words appear, one reading diagonally from top left to bottom right, and the other reading diagonally from bottom left to top right.

DEHUMIDIFIES
MEGALOMANIAC
SUBCONTINENT
FAINTHEARTED
SEMICIRCULAR
ANTIMACASSAR
SCRATCHINESS
INGLORIOUSLY
TEMPERATURES
CANCELLATION
HORSEMANSHIP
CAMOUFLAGING

CRYPTOGRAM 2

MITZI CHRISTIANSEN KUEHL, USA

The following cryptogram is a straight substitution code in which each letter of the alphabet has been replaced by another. Start by solving the cryptogram, then follow the instructions given after the cryptogram to find a further keyed message.

I, SK YIGU MB YMCU P OUT, OUT, OIBU, EZPE'B WUHYK BLOFWX MW AFWU.   *OIQUOE QFOWB*

AFWU MB QFBEMW' IFE PYY IGUO…
                    VOIS *RPOIFBUY*,
        OITXUOB PWT ZPSSUOBEUMW

HU BZPYY ZPGU EI QFK AFWU BISU WUH RYIEZUB DFMEU BIIW.

To find the keywords (4'1, 4, 2), place the letters of the code opposite the corresponding letters of the alphabet. The keywords will become apparent between the first eight and the last eight letters of the alphabet.

	CODED TEXT
A	
B	
C	
D	
E	
F	
G	
H	
I	
J	
K	
L	
M	
N	
O	
P	
Q	
R	
S	
T	
U	
V	
W	
X	
Y	
Z	

2:1

MICHAEL N. VAN DER RIET, REPUBLIC OF SOUTH AFRICA

Each of the 10 words listed below can be matched with two of the diagrams. Your task is to allocate each word to the two diagrams with which it corresponds. Each diagram is used once only.

Cancer Chance Delta Diode Japan
Mercury Moon Quincunx Root Uranus

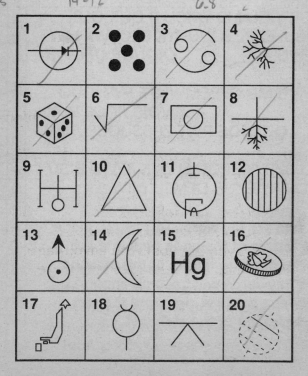

ODD ONE OUT 3

LLOYD KING, UK

Which is the odd one out?

Hawk, Alone, Pilot, Brief, Echo

Q62 ☆ **A67**

LETTER CHANGE

MITZI CHRISTIANSEN KUEHL, USA

In a letter change one single letter has been changed to make a new word – as in alter and after, for instance.

For example:

'You xxxxxx is getting worse again,'   *plaque*
The dentist said, severely.
'Avoid all sugar like the xxxyxx,   *plague*
And come to see me yearly.'

1.   The bistro had delicious food.
     The suitor, in xxxxxxxxx mood,
     Had played the host with savoir-faire
     And wined and dined his lady there.
     But morning saw a sobered swain
     Regard his budget with great pain.
     It clearly showed, on quick review,
     The evening was xxxyxxxxx, too!

2.   When darkness xxxxxx the house at night
     The xxxyxx perform a midnight rite.
     In measured movement two hands meet,
     Proclaim the time, and then retreat.

In the following puzzle only the seventh and
eighth letters in the nine-letter word change
places with the first letter. All the other letters
remain in the same position.

3.   The Order Lepidoptera
     Impaled upon a pin
     Or captured in a plastic base
     Engenders my chagrin.

     How better, on a summer day
     To see one xxyyyyy zx
     As free as it was meant to be:
     A gorgeous zyyyyyxxx!

4.   Harry Hankin, heavyweight
     Heed this xxxxxx xxxyxx:
     Henry VIII, who ate and ate
     Died a gross anomaly.

Q63 ☆☆☆ **A70**

SOMETHING IN COMMON

LLOYD KING, UK

What have these words in common?

Flowering, Hussar, Sparkle, Unoiled

'10' PUZZLE

MALCOLM GIRLING, UK

Fill in the missing signs to complete the equation below. The equation is evaluated strictly from left to right, and no two similar signs may appear consecutively. You have to use two each of the signs: plus, minus, multiply and divide.

$$1 ? 2 ? 3 ? 4 ? 5 ? 6 ? 7 ? 8 ? 9 = 10$$

MATCH PLAY 2

LLOYD KING, UK

Re-arrange four of the matches to make six squares. They must not overlap or be broken. Lateral thinking is required!

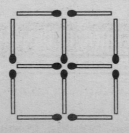

ONE MORE LETTER

ANDREW CHALLIS, UK

Ten words will fit into the grid, each word being an anagram of the word above it, plus one more letter. The extra letters to be added are listed in Column 1, but they are not in the correct order. A clue to the meaning of each word is given in Column 2, but these are in a different order again. Can you match the right letter in Column 1 with the right clue in Column 2 in their respective correct order to identify the 10 missing words?

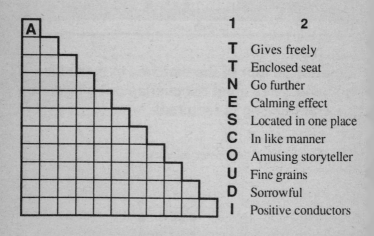

	1	2
	T	Gives freely
	T	Enclosed seat
	N	Go further
	E	Calming effect
	S	Located in one place
	C	In like manner
	O	Amusing storyteller
	U	Fine grains
	D	Sorrowful
	I	Positive conductors

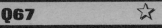
INTERLOCK

MITZI CHRISTIANSEN KUEHL, USA

In an interlock, several smaller words are
interspersed throughout a longer word. An
example of an interlock is battleships: bath
(xxxx), tip (yyy) and less (zzzz) – xxxyzzzxyyx.

'It's xxxxxxx,' the doctor said,
Demeanour sad and drawn.
'The zzz must promptly be removed;
We'll operate at dawn.'

So xxxyyyxzzzxxx the yyy:
Prognosis now, 'benign'.
The shovels filled the zzz right in,
The doctor's yard is fine.

RIDDLE

CHRIS BEDFORD, UK

What are you doing if you follow these
instructions?

Start by changing directions, then leave
nothing alone. Now make room for me, and
keep the thing at the end intact.

ODD ONE OUT 4

LLOYD KING, UK

Which is the odd one out?

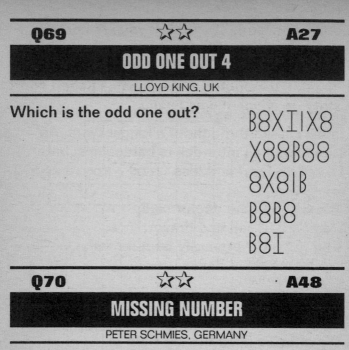

B8XIIX8
X88B88
8X8IB
B8B8
B8I

MISSING NUMBER

PETER SCHMIES, GERMANY

Study the array of numbers below and work out the missing number.

28	20	7
84	35	12
45	?	9

SF PUZZLE

AUDREY AUSTIN, AUSTRALIA

Re-arrange the given words, adding Ss and/or Fs as necessary to form complete new words. You can see how many letters there are in each word from the grid. If you are correct, the first letters of these new words, reading downwards, will spell out the name of a 1971 film and the author of the science fiction short story on which it was based.

1. No quiet
2. Ace tuned
3. To leer
4. At lime tag
5. Ingot
6. In gold
7. Ye live on
8. Marine root
9. Title
10. Toe
11. Anti cover
12. Enter Roy
13. Jupiter Nurd
14. Clay root
15. The anti
16. England we
17. Win during
18. Day trick
19. Give mat in
20. Diet can
21. Poor thin
22. Rat no
23. Mound can tile

VOWEL CHANGE

PETER SCHMIES, GERMANY

The vowels A, E, I, O, U can all be added to the letters B – L L to form the four-letter words BALL, BELL, BILL, BOLL and BULL. How many other such words can you find in which all five vowels can be inserted?

BRAINBENDERS

PETER SCHMIES, GERMANY

Study the following groups of numbers and work out the missing number in each case.

1.	13	12	5		2.	3	2	2
	17	15	8			6	20	4
	25	24	?			12	25	64
	29	21	20			6	10	?

THE ODD COUPLE

LLOYD KING, UK

Which is the odd one out?

1. Hod and colt
2. Trial and past
3. Lank and fire
4. Bus and yell
5. Hike and seed

ANAGRAMS 2

RAY WILBER, USA

An anagram is an apposite re-arrangement of a phrase. For example, I AM A PENCIL DOT is an anagram of A DECIMAL POINT (1, 7, 5). The numbers indicate the number of letters in each word of the answer. An asterisk (*) before a number indicates a capitalized word. Some of the answers will be more familiar than others but all will bear some relationship to the original.

1. SO REAL NICE CRAB (6, 8)
2. MIGHT BREW OLD TEA (3, 4, 8)
3. BIRD (BERTH'S ON A TREE) (3, 5, 9)
4. EARTHFAST, SO VILE (4, 4, 2, 5)
5. THEN WINGED RAYS OF RED (3, 4-8, 4)
6. HOT NETHER (3, 6)
7. ITCH? OH, GEE! (3, 6)
8. O, GEN. MIGHT RATE TOPS (*6, *5, *6)
9. ALERTNESS IN BOY'S ADVENTURES
(*8, *6, 2, *9)
10. AH, SPOTTING HOT NEWS! (3, *10, *4)
11. THIS TEAM'S TAME AND DOCILE (3, 12, 7)
12. THEIR LEGS AR' ALL QUITE NEAT (3, 11, 9)
13. SLING BILGE AT (*12)
14. GET NOTHING! HEARD ME? (3, 3, 2, 3, 6)
15. 'N' LEO HAS THEIRS (3, 4'1, 5)
16. HEAT IS NORM (2, 8)
17. COUNT'M A LIAR (11)

CONTAINER

MITZI CHRISTIANSEN KUEHL, USA

In a container one or more short words are contained within a longer word. The word seafarer, for example, contains the words seer and afar – se(afar)er.

Yyxxxxxyyy their fans in vain,
Courtesans become chagrined;
Xxxxx improprieties,
Yyyyy discretion to the wind.

18 TREES PUZZLE

CLARENCE KOHRING, USA

A gardener has a total of 18 trees, which he wishes to plant in straight rows of five trees in each row. In addition, he sets himself the task of planting the trees in such a way that he will obtain the maximum number of rows of five trees that are possible with such an arrangement. How did he achieve his task?

ANSWERS

A1   FATUITOUS PECULIARITY   Q13

Every word begins with the last letter of the preceding word, and the last letter in the sentence is also the first.

A2   FIND THE LADY   Q43

Taking A = 1, B = 2 and so on, each of the words given totals 100, except BALALAIKA, which is 50. My darling is of course CLEMENTINE.

She is THIRTY, was born under TAURUS and has the most beautiful eyes of AQUAMARINE. I met her on a WEDNESDAY, and it was as if I had been struck by a bolt of LIGHTNING.

A3   STRAIGHT AND TRUE NUMBERS   Q56

29 (TWENTY NINE) is the only straight and true number in English. In Dutch, only 10 (TIEN) is straight and true. We are unable to find straight and true numbers in other languages.

A4   THINKING MAN'S SERIES   Q35

BEDE: taking A = 1, B = 2, etc. the names given total successively 100, 81, 64, 49, 36 and 25 – i.e., descending square numbers. The name BEDE totals 16.

A5   MANAGRA PARIS   Q22

1.	Thicken	7.	Kitchen
2.	License	9.	Silence
3.	Monograph	17.	Phonogram
4.	Sleuth	25.	Hustle
5.	Cretins	16.	Cistern
6.	Hustlers	23.	Ruthless
8.	Matins	22.	Mantis
10.	Dreamer	20.	Rearmed
11.	Direct	21.	Credit
12.	Conifers	18.	Forensic
13.	Reacted	27.	Catered
14.	Entrap	19.	Parent
15.	Affair	24.	Raffia
26.	Stripes	28.	Persist

A6	LOGICAL PROGRESSION	Q3

Incest: each word starts with the letter whose position in the alphabet coincides with the number of letters in the preceding word. Occultism has nine letters; therefore the next word starts with the ninth letter of the alphabet, I.

A7	WORD SEQUENCE	Q47

Iron: bAsE, mInOr, UpstArt, hElIcOn, cUrAtE, IrOn

A8	'10' PUZZLE	Q64

$$1 \div 2 \times 3 - 4 + 5 \times 6 - 7 \div 8 + 9 = 10$$

A9	CROSSNUMBER	Q25

A10	VOWEL CHANGE	Q72

pack, peck, pick, pock, puck
last, lest, list, lost, lust
mass, mess, miss, moss, muss
band, bend, bind, bond, bund
rack, reck, rick, rock, ruck

ALL'S WELL THAT ENDS WELL
ANTONY AND CLEOPATRA
AS YOU LIKE IT
THE COMEDY OF ERRORS
CORIOLANUS
CYMBELINE
HAMLET
JULIUS CAESAR
KING LEAR
LOVE'S LABOUR'S LOST
MACBETH
MEASURE FOR MEASURE
THE MERCHANT OF VENICE
THE MERRY WIVES OF WINDSOR

A MIDSUMMER NIGHT'S DREAM
MUCH ADO ABOUT NOTHING
OTHELLO
PERICLES
ROMEO AND JULIET
THE TAMING OF THE SHREW
THE TEMPEST
TIMON OF ATHENS
TITUS ANDRONICUS
TROILUS AND CRESSIDA
TWELFTH NIGHT
THE TWO GENTLEMEN OF VERONA
THE WINTER'S TALE

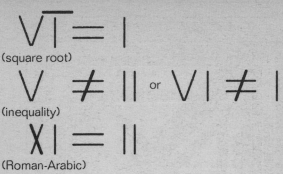

(square root)

(inequality)

(Roman-Arabic)

(Boolean algebra 1 or 1 = 1)

B: starting with a 7-segment LED-display 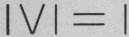 the puzzle consists of the unused segments when displaying the numbers 0-7.

2: the others are familiar pairings in which the positions of two letters have been swapped: hot and cold, rank and file, buy and sell, hide and seek.

Ate: Eyot (Consumed: Island)
Buy: Bye (Bribe: Run)
Cite: Sight (Summon: View)
Dew: Due (Moisture: Owed)
Eye: Aye (Keep in view: Indeed)
Furs: Furze (Wraps: Gorse)
Guys: Guise (Chaps: Behaviour)
Heal: Heel (Cure: Spur)
Ide: Eyed (Fish: Looked)

Jam: Jamb (Conserve: Post)
Knead: Need (Mould: Require)
Loot: Lute (Ransack: Stringed instrument)
Mynah: Minor (Bird: Junior)
Nee: Neigh (Born: Cry)
Or: Awe (Alternative: Wonder)
Pare: Pear (Trim: Fruit)
Quay: Key (Wharf: Island)
Rows: Rose (Ranks: Flower)
Seize: Sees (Grab: Regards)
Two: Too (Pair: Also)
Use: Ewes (Employ: Sheep)
Vault: Volt (Cellar: Gait)
Wheel: Weal (Firework: Streak)
Yore: Yaw (Long ago: Zigzag)

A16	**FARMER GILES'S FIELD**	**Q42**

45 sheep

If s = a daily sheep ration of grass
  c = a daily cow ration of grass
  G = the initial grass on the field
  g = the daily grass grown on the field

then
$6 \times 60s = 360s = G + 6g$
$3 \times 30c = 90c = G + 3g$

so (eliminate G)
  $G = 360s - 6g$
$90c = 360s - 6g + 3g = 360s - 3g$
  $g = 120s - 30c$

We also know that
$g = 20s + 10c$

so
$120s - 30c = 20s + 10c$
    $5s = 2c$

and therefore
$g = 20s + (5/2 \times 10)s = 45s$

In other words, the grass grown daily on the field is enough
to support 45 sheep permanently.

ADO	RAT	ION	BAY	ONE	TED
CAN	DID	ATE	DEN	TIS	TRY
FUR	THE	RED	GOD	FAT	HER
INN	OVA	TOR	NEW	SPA	PER
PAR	SON	AGE	WAR	RAN	TEE

1. Monocular; 2. Hetero-; 3. Chandler; 4. Chimaera;
5. Galena; 6. Nephro-; 7. Eolian; 8. Procrustean; 9. Carroll;
10. Palaeo-; 11. Dendroid; 12. Lethean

Rating:
2 - 3 average; 4 - 5 good; 6 - 7 very good; 8 - 9 excellent;
10 - 11 exceptional; 12 superbrain

At the eleventh footfall the combined number of steps taken is 12, because the last steps of father and son sound together. The son is smaller and so takes more strides. Side by side, both cover the same distance. Therefore, in number of strides:

$S + F = 12$
$S > F$

To meet the simultaneity criterion, there are only two mathematical possibilities for the number of strides:

$S = 11$ and $F = 1$ or $S = 7$ and $F = 5$

No man can stride 770cm, therefore father's stride is:
$$\frac{70 \times 7}{5} = 98cm$$

Note: $S = 10$ and $F = 2$ is not a possible answer because their feet would have touched the ground simultaneously *before* – i.e., after the son's fifth and the father's first stride; but the question clearly states that their feet touch the ground simultaneously *for the first time*. For similar reasons, $S = 9$ and $F = 3$, and $S = 8$ and $F = 4$ are not correct either.

9 rows; there are two possible solutions.

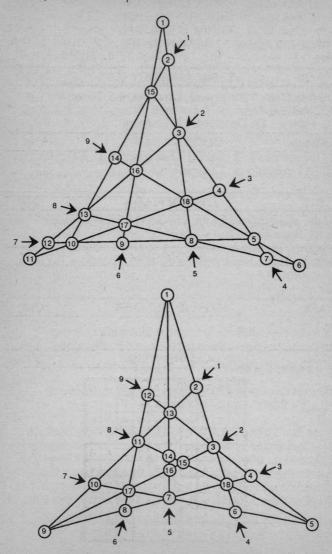

1. look before you leAP, PLEase; 2. charMED LARge snakes; 3. coP RUN East; 4. hoME LONg before nightfall; 5. reSULT, AN Agent; 6. loan-sharK – I WIsh; 7. baIL – I MEt a man; 8. in the jUG. 'LIar!'; 9. oGRE ENGAGEd our attention; 10. braT – ANGER IN Every; 11. huMAN DARINg; 12. dRAM, BUT A Nice; 13. heM ANGOra?; 14. HoW A TERM ELONgated at Eton; 15. heP LUMinous trousers; 16. hath I PINE – APPLE jack; 17. kORAN GEn if every Arabian; 18. the ManaGUA VAndals team; 19. a CuBAN, AN Art critic; 20. official baR HUB ARBiter.

Echo: in the other words the first and last letters are the same number of letters apart as they are in the alphabet.

A: the shapes spell the word LOGIC in reverse order.

$324^2 = 104976$

48: $(13-11) \times (16 + 8)$

I	D	L	Y	B	A	N	S	H	E
S	O	U	A	L	M	E	P	I	C
L	E	G	M	O	P	W	A	S	H
E	N	D	S	W	I	T	U	F	O
V	I	E	O	F	T	S	C	A	G
O	P	A	L	I	S	H	T	R	Y
W	A	R	D	E	N	Y	H	O	P
A	S	K	U	R	E	C	O	L	D
C	H	O	P	A	R	I	N	E	U
T	Y	P	E	M	O	A	K	G	B

B̶8̶X̶I̶I̶X̶8̶   The others are reflected words.

$SEEK_{10} = 2337$:

$SEEK_7 + SEEK_6 + SEEK_5 = 54321$
$6546 + 14453 + 33322 = 54321$

To express 2337 (a decimal number) in base 7, we proceed as follows:

2337 divided by 7 is 333, remainder 6;
 333 divided by 7 is 47, remainder 4;
  47 divided by 7 is   6, remainder 5;

so the resulting number is 6546 (and similarly for the other bases).

There is another value for SEEK that yields interesting results: if $SEEK_{10} = 1006$, $SEEK_7 = 2635$, $SEEK_6 = 4354$ and $SEEK_5 = 13011$; the sum of these last three numbers is 20000 – *if* we treat them as decimal numbers, that is! Should we choose to treat them as *octal* (base 8) numbers, however, this is what we get:

$$2635_8 = 1437_{10}$$
$$4354_8 = 2284_{10}$$
$$13011_8 = 5631_{10} +$$
$$\overline{}$$
$$9362_{10}$$

The resulting total, 9362, may not seem very special … until we express it, too, as an octal number: 22222_8!

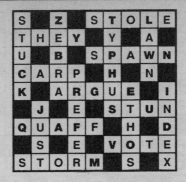

| A30 | CONTAINER | Q76 |

Fluttering, utter, fling

| A31 | NUMBERS | Q29 |

4: each number corresponds with the number of letters in the previous number.

| A32 | 2 : 1 | Q60 |

3 and 20 CANCER, 5 and 16 CHANCE, 4 and 10 DELTA, 1 and 11 DIODE, 7 and 17 JAPAN, 15 and 18 MERCURY, 12 and 14 MOON, 2 and 19 QUINCUNX, 6 and 8 ROOT, 9 and 13 URANUS

| A33 | SERIES | Q44 |

12: divide 25 by 1, 2, 3, 4 and so on; the remainders yield the given series.

| A34 | WORDS | Q11 |

Seam: read the words in descending order, paying attention to their sounds only. The proverb 'things are not always what they seem' is revealed.

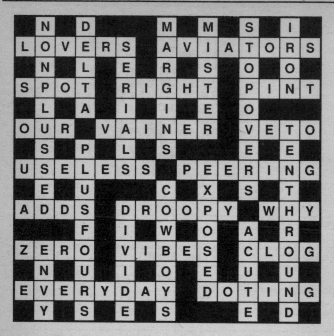

1. $7 - 7^2 + 24^2 = 25^2$
2. $8 - \sqrt[3]{2 \times 4 \times 64}$

The two words reading diagonally are SCHOOLMASTER and SEISMOLOGIST.

```
S U B C O N T I N E N T
S C R A T C H I N E S S
D E H U M I D I F I E S
C A M O U F L A G I N G
I N G L O R I O U S L Y
C A N C E L L A T I O N
M E G A L O M A N I A C
A N T I M A C A S S A R
H O R S E M A N S H I P
F A I N T H E A R T E D
T E M P E R A T U R E S
S E M I C I R C U L A R
```

Our best solution goes up to 1954. Can you equal or beat it?

1901-1954

3	8	7	6	4
4	3	2	4	9
9	2	9	0	8
0	1	5	1	7
6	3	9	4	1

1. AERODYNAMICALLY (IRK)
2. CINEMATOGRAPHER (HIM)
3. MISAPPREHENSION (SHE)
4. DISADVANTAGEOUS (BUG)
5. NEIGHBOURLINESS (CAN)

The sixth 15-letter word, formed by combining the five unused three-letter words in brackets above, is BUCKINGHAMSHIRE.

The two related solutions are:

```
 74890    and:    34890
 30737 +          70373 +
 ------           ------
105627           105263
```

The third solution is:

```
 67590
 40646 +
 ------
108236
```

---

1. Cancer borealis (a species of crab found off New England); 2. The wild bergamot (a plant used to make herb tea); 3. The robin redbreast; 4. This vale of tears; 5. The rosy-fingered dawn; 6. The hornet; 7. The chigoe (a tropical flea, the female of which burrows into the host's skin); 8. George Smith Patton; 9. Treasure Island by Stevenson; 10. The Washington Post; 11. The domesticated animals; 12. The equilateral triangles; 13. Billingsgate; 14. The dog in the manger; 15. The lion's share; 16. An isotherm; 17. Calumniator

---

An **eagle pie** meal **at Reeth aler**ted a man na**med Lev**i and friends to **real**ize how **won**derful alternativ**e cu**isine ta**sted. 'I me**ant t**o bol**t down a **cob of ranc**id butte**r and a ric**h, **mil**ky **far**mhouse cheese for dessert, but **Mark**, **Joey**, **Tom an**d **Louis**e recommended gra**pes o**r turni**p ice** cream!'

Eagle, Pie, Lat, Ree, Thaler, Dam, Anna, Lev, Real, Won, Ecu, As, Dime, Obol, Cob, Franc, Rand, Daric, Mil, Far, Mark, Joey, Toman, Louis, Peso, Pice

A43	SEQUENCE	Q21

What: the first 17 letters are repeated in the same order.

A44	FIGURE IT OUT	Q45

D: a sequence is formed by the letters V, W, X, Y and Z contained within the shapes.

A45	LETTER DELETION	Q40

1. soldier, solder; 2. portable, potable

A46	DOMINOES	Q2

5	1	0	3	3	6	4	5
4	5	6	0	4	2	3	5
4	1	5	0	3	5	4	6
6	2	2	5	0	2	6	5
6	2	3	6	3	0	3	1
1	6	2	1	0	1	1	4
0	4	0	2	3	2	1	4

A47	CRYPTIC WORD SQUARE 1	Q12

L	I	S	P	E	D
I	M	P	O	S	E
S	P	A	R	T	A
P	O	R	T	A	L
E	S	T	A	T	E
D	E	A	L	E	R

25: divide the left-hand number by the number on the right and multiply by 5.

The missing words are: MIKE, INDIA, CHARLIE, PAPA, UNIFORM, HOTEL, ROMEO, JULIET, NOVEMBER, X-RAY, ALPHA, KILO, OSCAR, YANKEE, DELTA, WHISKEY, ZULU, GULF, SIERRA, LIMA, QUEBEC, VICTOR, FOXTROT, ECHO, TANGO, BRAVO.
These words are, of course, the phonetic communications alphabet.

1. Stow; 2. The plot thickens; 3. Entangle; 4. Blessing in disguise; 5. No entry; 6. Innuendo; 7. Storm in a tea cup; 8. Agape; 9. Naughty; 10. Tenet; 11. Nothing out of the ordinary; 12. Comedy

17	5	10	21	12
4	23	14	8	16
13	7	1	25	19
11	24	18	9	3
20	6	22	2	15

14	11	20	5	15
4	22	13	23	3
24	7	1	25	8
6	9	19	10	21
17	16	12	2	18

It is a 24-hour clock!

1. Mediterranean fruit fly;   2. The wind chill factor

1. Question, 2. Unaffected, 3. Effortless, 4. Stalagmite,
5. Tossing, 6. Folding, 7. Offensively, 8. Reformation,
9. Leftist, 10. Offset, 11. Vociferant, 12. Effrontery,
13. Jurisprudent, 14. Olfactory, 15. Hesitant,
16. Newfangled, 17. Windsurfing, 18. Yardstick,
19. Negativism, 20. Distance, 21. Hoofprint, 22. Affront,
23. Malfunctioned

The film is *Quest for Love*, from the short story by John Wyndham.

A55　　　**CRYPTIC WORD SQUARE 2**　　　**Q30**

C	A	M	E	R	A
A	M	U	S	E	S
M	U	S	C	A	T
E	S	C	A	P	E
R	E	A	P	E	R
A	S	T	E	R	N

A56　　　　　**ONE MORE LETTER**　　　　　**Q66**

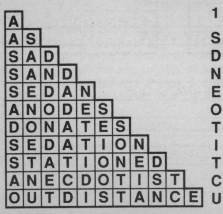

		1	2
	S	In like manner
	D	Sorrowful
	N	Fine grains
	E	Enclosed seat
	O	Positive conductors
	T	Gives freely
	I	Calming effect
	T	Located in one place
	C	Amusing storyteller
	U	Go further

| A57 | THE COLLECTOR'S BEQUEST | Q54 |

3121: 3121 − 1 = 3120 x 4/5 =
      2496 − 1 = 2495 x 4/5 =
      1996 − 1 = 1995 x 4/5 =
      1596 − 1 = 1595 x 4/5 =
      1276 − 1 = 1275 x 4/5 =
      1020 ÷ 5 = 204 for each daughter

| A58 | CRYPTOGRAM 1 | Q17 |

Mnemonic devices and memory tricks
Are fabulous helpers when nothing else sticks.
But then, to remember mnemonics I find,
They jam up the circuits in my addled mind.

| A59 | LETTER ADDITION | Q46 |

1. curry favour, curry flavour; 2. celerity, celebrity; 3. sum it, summit

| A60 | SQUARE AND SQUARE ALIKE | Q33 |

D: it is the only box in which a dot can be put in both two squares and a triangle!

| A61 | RIDDLE | Q68 |

Making something out of nothing

| A62 | CHARADES | Q24 |

1. at, ten, at, at, dance, at, dance, attendance; 2. gent, pungent, pun; 3. together, to, get, to, get, her, her;
4. kidnapped, kid, napped; 5. tenant, lieu, lieutenant;
6. sputter, putter, utter; 7. tis, sue, tissue, issue

| A63 | CODED MESSAGE | Q51 |

'Many a man owes his success to his first wife and his second wife to his success.'
Jim Backus

The code is:

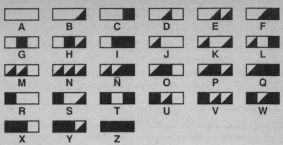

A   B   C   D   E   F
G   H   I   J   K   L
M   N   Ñ   O   P   Q
R   S   T   U   V   W
X   Y   Z

T	H	S	M	F	T	W	C
N	S			C	T	V	T	E
R	N	G	L	R	N	U	O
M		B	R	S	O		O
S		S	Q		E		U
	R	N	I		E	I	A
M	B	U		A	U		E
R	I	A	U	A	E	U	E

The grid has eight squares across and eight down. 8 x 8 = 64, a square number. The top left section contains 36 consonants and blanks. 36 is a triangular number (8 + 7 + 6 ... + 2 + 1). The bottom right section contains 28 vowels and blanks. 28 is the next smallest triangular number (7 + 6 + 5 ... + 2 + 1). The consonants and vowels are in order when they are read conventionally in each section, and the mix of consonants, vowels and blanks gives the statement: 'The sum of two consecutive triangular numbers is a square number.' The grid shows the proof of the theorem.

Meeny has a probable advantage of 17/216, about 7.87 per cent.

The probability of a number appearing face up:

	3 times	2 times	Once	None
$(1/6 + 5/6)^3$ =	1/216	+ 15/216	+ 75/216	+ 125/216

In every 216 tosses, Moe can expect to win:

    1 x $3 =   3
    15 x $2 = 30
    75 x $1 = 75   Total $108

However, he wins his $108 on only 91 throws (1 + 15 + 75). On the other 125 throws he loses ($125). Therefore, Meeny can expect to gain $17 every 216 throws.

This result may seem strange at first: it would seem that Moe's changing the rules has improved the odds in his favour. This is in fact true. So we have to conclude that, under Meeny's original rules, the game was not even at all!

Under the original rules, Moe would lose if die #1 did not show the number he had chosen (P = 5/6) *and* die #2 did not show that number *and* die #3 did not show that number. The probability of this happening is $(5/6)^3$ or 125/216, so Moe would lose a dollar in 125 throws out of 216 and would win in 91 throws out of 216. In 216 throws, Meeny could expect to gain $34.

Under the new rules, Moe gets an *extra* dollar when his chosen number faces up *twice* (which will happen in 15 throws out of 216), and *two* extra dollars if it faces up three times (once in every 216 throws); these $15 + $2 explain the difference between the $17 and the $34 Meeny could expect to win.

A66	TRANSPOSALS	Q8

1. spectre, sceptre, respect; 2. meteor, remote; 3. drain, nadir, ranid; 4. shingle (a small sign fixed outside the office of a US doctor, lawyer, etc.), English; 5. hustle, sleuth; 6. rate, stigma, magistrate; 7. admirer, married; 8. assuage, a, a, sausage, guess; 9. October, all, collaborate, a; 10. cat, rule, nibs, inscrutable; 11. a, winter, eve, interweave; 12. mouse, baits, abstemious; 13. curmudgeon, cur, mud, curmudgeon, cur, gone; 14. nights, goblins, ghosts, sights; 15. silent, listen, tinsel, enlist; 16. continued, unnoticed

---

A67	LETTER CHANGE	Q62

1. expansive, expensive; 2. cloaks, clocks; 3. flutter by, butterfly; 4. homely, homily

---

A68	ODD ONE OUT 2	Q27

Batch: the first, third and fifth letters in all the other words are in alphabetical order.

| A69 | FRAGMENTED QUOTATION | Q32 |

'We are not interested in the possibilities of defeat.'

Queen Victoria, 1899

| A70 | SOMETHING IN COMMON | Q63 |

Each contains a mammal in reverse: wolf, ass, elk, lion.

| A71 | ODD ONE OUT 1 | Q9 |

Edinburgh: the others are the names of British prime ministers.

| A72 | INTERLOCK | Q67 |

Serious, pit, serendipitous, end, pit

| A73 | CONSONANT LOSS | Q57 |

1. Lawyer, 2. Dentist, 3. Model, 4. Fireman, 5. Postman,
6. Builder, 7. Croupier, 8. Bookmaker, 9. Manicurist,
10. Journalist, 11. Upholsterer, 12. Beautician, 13. Typist,
14. Doctor, 15. Nurse, 16. Farmer, 17. Policeman,
18. Welder, 19. Carpenter, 20. Jockey, 21. Bus Driver,
22. Jeweller, 23. Accountant, 24. Prison Warder,
25. Engineer, 26. Hairdresser

| A74 | FRACTIONS | Q31 |

$$\frac{49}{98} = \frac{1}{2} \qquad \frac{19}{95} = \frac{1}{5} \qquad \frac{26}{65} = \frac{2}{5}$$

| A75 | ALPHABET CROSSWORD 2 | Q49 |

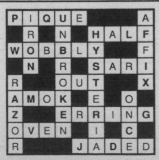

'O, my love is like a red, red, rose, that's newly sprung in June.'   *Robert Burns*

'June is bustin' out all over...'

From *Carousel*,
Rodgers and Hammerstein

We shall have to buy June some new clothes quite soon.

KEYWORDS: MACY'S WILL DO.

The matches now form an additional square in the centre.

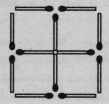

UNSOLVED PUZZLES

'It may well be doubted whether human
ingenuity can construct an enigma of the kind
which human ingenuity may not, by proper
application, resolve.'

Edgar Allan Poe

The puzzles in this section have just one thing
in common: they are all as yet unsolved.
Some are old, some are new, some are
famous and some unknown. How long they
will remain unsolved after the publication of
this book we can only guess. As one
contributor put it: 'It all depends on who you
ask. I had a geometric problem for about 30
years until I gave it to a new acquaintance…
He came back with the answer in 3 days!'

An Unsolved Charade

During the nineteenth century, Winthorpe Mackworth Praed, an English author who is best remembered for his humorous verse, tried his hand at puzzle compiling when he composed the following charade without ever revealing his intended solution. Although puzzle historians have reluctantly accepted 'good night' as the best answer, the charade nevertheless became quite controversial because no one could really agree. Some years ago, Martin Thiebaut, a Luxembourg member of I.S.P.E., published the charade in the I.S.P.E. journal *Telicom* and invited members to propose alternative solutions, but none was forthcoming. Even so, we are including the charade in our section of unsolved puzzles in the hope that one day a more feasible solution than 'good night' may be put forward.

Sir Hilary charged at Agincourt;
  Sooth, 'twas an awful day!
And though in that old age of sport
The rufflers of the camp and court
  Had little time to pray.
'Tis said Sir Hilary muttered there
Two syllables by way of prayer:
My First to all the brave and proud
  Who see tomorrow's sun:
My Next, with her cold and quiet cloud,
To those who find their dewy shroud
  Before today's be done:
And both together to all blue eyes
That weep when a warrior nobly dies.

The Cube-corner Diophantine

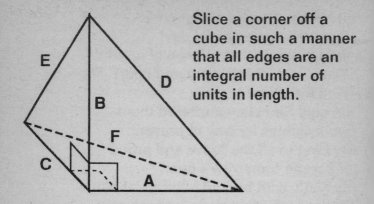

Slice a corner off a cube in such a manner that all edges are an integral number of units in length.

This puzzle was sent to us by R. O. Whitaker, a retired electrical researcher living in Florida, USA, and a member of I.S.P.E

No solution has been found since the problem was proposed by Mr Whitaker in *Telicom*, the I.S.P.E. journal, several years ago. Mr Whitaker comments: 'I have worked like the dickens on it, but have never solved it. Two people proffered answers to the problem – obtained by successive approximation using a computer or calculator. Essentially their solution was the program for the computer. I have tried for an old-fashioned analytical solution.'

Fermat's Last Theorem

There are many instances where the sum of two square numbers is equal to another square number, but there are no instances where the sum of two cube numbers is equal to another cube number.

This is the basis of Fermat's Last Theorem: a simple statement, the proof of which has eluded mathematicians for over three hundred years.

Pierre de Fermat was a seventeenth-century mathematician who founded number theory and, with Blaise Pascal, probability theory. When, shortly before his death in 1665, Fermat scribbled a note in the margin of a textbook, he created what was to become probably the most famous of all unsolved puzzles by claiming to have discovered a proof of the theorem: $X^n + Y^n = Z^n$ is impossible for positive integers X, Y, Z and n where n is greater than 2. 'But,' Fermat wrote, 'the margin is too narrow to contain it.' There is an infinite number of answers for $X^n + Y^n = Z^n$ where n = 2 – for example, 3^2 (9) + 4^2 (16) = 5^2 (25). However, no one has found an answer for $X^3 + Y^3 = Z^3$ or for any other indices above 2; but, on the other hand, neither has anyone discovered a formula that proves that it cannot be done. Computers have tried and reached enormous numbers for X, Y and Z, and also for n, but to no avail, so the general belief is that, although conclusive mathematical proof is still awaited, there are no numbers that will satisfy the equation.

We are grateful to 'Top One Percent Society' member First Lt Roderick D. Wingfield for suggesting that this famous unsolved puzzle be included in this section.

An Unsolved Number Series

What is the next number in the series 2, 4, 6, 9, 12, 17, 20, 25, 28, 31, 34 ?

The series originally appeared in *Superforce*, a book by Paul Davies, a Professor of Applied Mathematics, published by Simon and Schuster. In 1985 a group of Spanish High-IQ society members became so intrigued why, after much collective mental exertion, they could not find a solution to this puzzle that the President of Spanish Mensa, Antonio Casao Ibáñez, wrote to Professor Davies for confirmation, or otherwise, of their conclusions.

Their first thought was of a possible error on the part of Professor Davies and they produced a similar series by adding to the series of natural progressive integers that of prime ones:

1	2	3	4	5	6	7	8	9	10	11
1	2	3	5	7	11	13	17	19	21	23+

2	4	6	9	12	17	20	25	28	31	34

Their deliberate error was to include 21 in the series of prime numbers. Was it possible that

Professor Davies had suffered a similar lapse? However, there was one flaw in their reasoning: 1 is not a prime number (a prime number is an integer above 1 that cannot be factorized into other integers but is divisible only by itself and by 1, such as 2, 3, 5, 7 and 11), so surely this could not be the explanation.

In his reply to the Spanish Mensans Professor Davies deepened the mystery when he commented: 'When my attention was first drawn to the 21, I went back to my original hand script, because I had forgotten the solution to the puzzle. To my horror I could not find the key to the series, which I recalled scribbling in a margin [shades of Fermat's Last Theorem!]. I then embarked on a long and arduous study to try and solve my own puzzle. Eventually I came to your conclusion that the 21 must be an error, though it was too late to change the Spanish translation. However, I'm not *completely* sure it's an error, so if you can ever find a solution…'

So the mystery remains. Does the series contain a number of errors so that there is no possible solution, or is there, in fact, some forgotten logic behind the sequence waiting to be re-discovered?

Fermat's Lost Algorithm

Newman's *World of Mathematics* contains the following item, which we include in our section of unsolved puzzles because the explanation is not known today, although it must have been known several hundred years ago: 'Accordingly, it is still a source of wonder that Fermat replied without a moment's hesitation to a letter which asked whether 100895598169 was prime, that it was the product of 898423 and 112303 and that each of these numbers was prime.'

Fermat must presumably have known an algorithm (a procedural model for complicated calculations) that enabled him to produce his answer so quickly, but this is now lost with time. To many people, including Mel Bebee, a Texan High-IQ society member who is attempting to find the 'recipe' again, it is a fascinating 'unsolved puzzle', and we are grateful to Mr Bebee for bringing it to our attention.

Hiding a Ball

How many balls does it take to hide a ball?

All the balls are identical, hard, ideal balls, and the target ball is considered hidden if, and only if, any straight line from any point on the target ball must pass through, or at least touch, another ball before it can reach an observer outside the matrix.

Compiled in 1983 by an Australian Mensan, Michael F. Yonwin, this puzzle has still to be solved to the satisfaction of its author. Mr Yonwin comments: 'This is straight-out solid geometry. In two dimensions, six circles will hide a circle; but in three dimensions, it is fiendishly difficult, and requires at least 98 balls – and I was never satisfied that they quite did the job. I could not prove it to my own satisfaction. Incidentally, the problem can be extended to n dimensions, and presumably a function exists giving the solutions, but I didn't even attempt to find it!'

ABOUT IQ TESTING

The earliest known attempt to rank people in terms of intelligence dates to the Chinese Mandarin system, when studying the works of Confucius enabled successful candidates to enter the public service. Great care was exercised to guarantee fairness to every candidate by employing an amanuensis to copy out each paper, so that no one's handwriting could be recognized and no favouritism would be shown. The top 1 per cent of candidates were successful in progressing to the next stage, where they would again be run off against each other, and the procedure was then repeated through a third layer of selection. Thus, the chosen candidates were in the top 1 per cent of the top 1 per cent of the top 1 per cent. Those who had been successful in the first test by some stroke of fortune would have faced an uphill battle against a field of genuinely able candidates and would have been eliminated with further testing, as would those wrongly placed for the third test. The Mandarin system worked as a purely administrative system and survived a millennium. However, critics claim it was essentially anti-creative in nature and, as a result, China remained a largely static society during this period. A parallel can be seen in Europe during the Middle Ages, when the works of Aristotle and Plato dominated men's minds in a similar way.

It was this reverence for ancient fact that led

mid-nineteenth-century psychiatrists to use information-loaded tests to assess the intelligence of their clients. Later, psychologists sought the basis of individual differences largely in terms of speed of performance at simple tasks. The assumption that reflex speed might hold the key proved a forlorn hope, yet the concept of mental speed has remained and is largely correct if applied to 'higher' tasks. Furneaux, around 1930, demonstrated that a relationship did exist between 'power', meaning the absolute difficulty of an item, and 'speed', meaning the time a person required to solve it. By increasing item difficulty by 30 per cent, you double the time required to solve it, but a 60 per cent increase increases the time fivefold. It was an Englishman, Sir Francis Galton, who was to give the movement experimental form with his Anthropomorphical Laboratory, and it is to Galton that we owe the basis of our interpretations in the form of the statistical concept of correlation.

Around the turn of the century, Alfred Binet and Theodore Simon were commissioned by the French government to construct tests to eliminate from the French educational system unfortunate children who did not achieve a sufficiently high mark to be considered able to benefit from it. They chose to measure intelligence at its own level and their tests provided a wide range of different types of items for inclusion. The concept of 'intelligence quotient' was unknown until

Stanford University translated the Binet test into English and added the concept of the ratio of mental age to chronological age, multiplied by 100. Thus a child of six years of age who successfully passed a test of an eight-year-old would possess an IQ of 8 divided by 6, multiplied by 100 – that is, an IQ of 133 – but a child of nine able to cope only with a test designed for a six-year-old would have an IQ of 67. From this developed the modern concept of adult IQ. Mental age remains constant in development to about the age of 13, after which it is shown to slow up further; and beyond the age of 18, little or no improvement is found. Adults had, therefore, to be judged on an IQ test whose average score was 100, and the results graded above and below this norm according to known scores.

Like most distributions found in nature, the distribution of IQ takes the form of a fairly regular bell curve. On the Stanford-Binet intelligence scale half of the population fall between 90 and 110 IQ (half of them above 100 and half of them below), 25 per cent score above 110, 11 per cent above 120, 3 per cent above 130 and 0.6 per cent above 140. Only one person in a thousand will have an IQ of 150, and one in ten thousand 160. At the opposite end of the curve, the same kind of proportion occurs. (In reality, things are not quite so simple as more men score in the very high ranges than women, and fewer women score in the very low ranges than men.)

The first IQ testing on a mass scale was carried out by the US Army during World War I. Out of this grew an attempt to analyse copious amounts of data. Personality tests, or character tests, were soon to follow, and what could not be explained away in terms of IQ was put down to aptitude and character. Just as psychologists had struggled to define their concept of intelligence, they now struggled to develop a concept of 'social intelligence'.

In the 1920s and 1930s studies began to define more closely the general concept of intelligence and to redefine the factors underlying that intelligence. What emerged was a recognition of fluid and crystallized intelligence. Fluid intelligence was measured by reference to spatial items (diagrams, drawings or pegs, for example); crystallized intelligence, on the other hand, was measured through language and number. At a high level, there is little overlap between the two. R. B. Cattell found that when his verbal and non-verbal tests were used within the top 5 per cent of the population, only 20 per cent overlap occurs, and Mensa (the High-IQ society) reported a 25 per cent overlap between its use of the Cattell and California tests for the 98th percentile (that is, the top 2 per cent of the population).

In the 1960s so-called tests of creative ability became popular and were intended to supplement intelligence testing. Gesalt and Jackson's tests of Divergent Ability required the subject to name as many uses as possible for common items like a comb, a brick or a piece of string. Although this idea is now said to 'have had its day', the findings were incorporated into the newer British Intelligence Test for children; its conclusions, however, have not been sustained.

Further development in the 1980s saw the widespread use of computers and databases, enabling data to be centralized for further access and analysis by psychologists. This decade also saw the development and acceptance of 'tailored testing theory' by Dr Vern William Urry, allowing the subject to be tested close to his individual level.

And so, as in all fields of science, research and development continue in the field of IQ testing. It should be borne in mind that, whatever the outcome, intelligence tests measure only the ability to reason. They do not measure the other qualities that are essential for success in life, such as character, personality, talent, persistence and application. People with a relatively low IQ should not be deterred. As long as they have a high sense of achievement and persistence, they have every chance of faring considerably better in life than the so-called 'brighter' people.

IQ TESTS

This test consists of a battery of 30 questions designed to test your powers of vocabulary, calculation and logical reasoning. There is a time limit of 60 minutes for completing the test in one sitting. You should keep strictly to the time limit because your score will be invalidated if it is exceeded, so work as quickly as possible.

The answers are on page 124.

1. From Bristol to Birmingham a motorist knows four different routes, from Birmingham to Sheffield he knows three different routes and from Sheffield to Carlisle he knows two different routes. How many routes does he know from Bristol to Carlisle?

2. Which two of the following words are closest in meaning?

book, motto, speech, sign,
maxim, memorandum

3. ARTIST is to PAINT as
TAILOR is to
(trousers, suit, fashion, cloth, scissors)

4. Which of the words in the brackets is opposite to the word in capitals?

ORDER (freedom, destroy, mob, chaos, rite)

5. Which number continues this sequence?

0.5, 0.55, 0.65. 0.8 ?

6. Which is the odd one out of the following?

tin, bronze, zinc, gold, silver

7.　CHEMISTRY is to SUBSTANCES as FAUNA is to
(plants, animals, reactions, soil, rocks)

8. Which of the words in the brackets is the closest in meaning to the word in capitals?

SWEET (plush, song, dulcet, rhythm, taste)

9. Which two of the following words have opposite meanings?

reply, resign, receive, employ, stay, resist

10. A batsman is out for 23 runs, which raises his batting average for the season from 15 to 16. How many would he have needed to score to have brought his average up to 18?

11. Which of the words in the brackets is opposite to the word in capitals?

SHIELD
(preserve, expose, strip, protect, proceed)

12. Four different coloured counters are placed in a row. The black counter is next to the blue counter but not next to the red. The red counter is not next to the white. Which counter is next to the white?

13. Which two of the following words are closest in meaning?

conserve, retreat, lose, haven, grace, garden

14. The houses in a street are numbered 1, 2, 3, 4, etc. up one side, then back down the other side. Opposite No. 11 is No. 28. How many houses are in the street?

15. Which is the odd one out of the following?

agenda, index, timetable, programme, schedule

16. Which two of the following words have opposite meanings?

unwell, fresh, sombre, unhappy, poor, bright

17. D.D.T. is to ABBREVIATION as
LASER is to (antithesis, epigram, word, acronym, imagery)

18. Which of the words in the brackets is closest in meaning to the word in capitals?

MOGUL
(tyrant, tycoon, terrorist, prince, soldier)

19. Which number continues this sequence?

0, 10, 10, 20, 30, 50 X

20. A train travelling at a speed of 45 m.p.h. enters a tunnel which is 1.5 miles long. The length of the train is 0.75 mile. How long does it take for all of the train to pass through the tunnel from the moment the front of the train enters the tunnel to the moment the rear emerges?

21. CASTLE is to DEFENCE as
THEATRE is to (audience, play, arena, entertainment, vaudeville)

22. Which of the following words are closest in meaning?

cascade, relish, fruitful, zest, mute, scene

23. Which is the odd one out of the following?

      angry, rash, volatile, fiery impetuous

24. Which of the words in the brackets is opposite to the word in capitals?

TACIT
(still, spoken, aware, vivid, irregular)

25. PATROL is to SECURITY as
      INSURANCE is to (finance, selling, protection, policy, money)

26. 'How much money have you?' asked Sid's father. 'Well,' replied Sid, 'if Jim gives me £4 he'll have half as much as Alf, but if Alf gives me £4 then the three of us will all have the same amount.' What was the total amount of money that Sid, Jim and Alf had between them?

27. Which word in the brackets is the closest in meaning to the word in capitals?

PARAMETER
(boundary, meaning, specification, law, pattern)

28. Which two of the following words have opposite meanings?

grave, worried, angry, facetious,
pleasant, fluent

29. Which is the odd one out of the following:

commotion, sound, bedlam, din, furore

30. If three lemons and four pears cost 40p and four lemons and three pears cost 37p, how much does one pear cost?

This is a culture-fair test, designed to test your powers of logical reasoning and your understanding of relationships, pattern and design. Study each display of diagrams and select the one option from each choice given. Study the instructions to each question.

You have a time limit of 20 minutes to complete the 10 questions in one sitting. You should keep strictly to the time limit, as your score will be invalidated if this is exceeded, so work as quickly as possible.

The answers are on page 124.

1. Which option – A, B, C, D or E – continues the sequence?

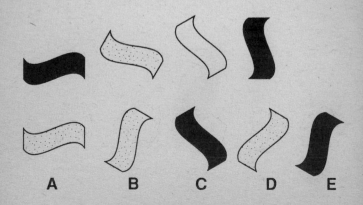

A   B   C   D   E

2. Which is the odd one out?

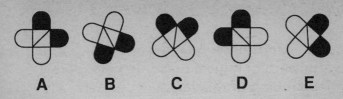

A   B   C   D   E

3.

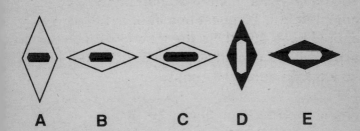

A   B   C   D   E

4.

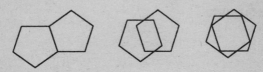

Which option below continues the above sequence?

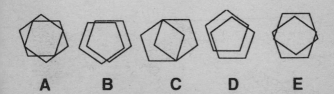

A   B   C   D   E

5. 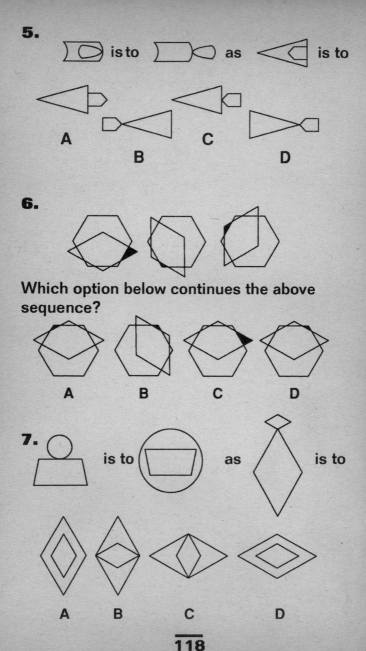 is to ☐◖ as ◁◁ is to

A

B

C

D

6.

Which option below continues the above sequence?

A   B   C   D

7. is to as is to

A   B   C   D

8. Which is the odd one out?

A B C

D E

9.

is to

as

is to

A B C D E

10.

is to

as

is to

A B C

One of the three words following is most closely related to the word in CAPITALS. Some words will have the same meaning, some the opposite, but many others will simply be **associated** with the key word. Underline or circle your choice from the three words given.

Give yourself any reasonable time to complete this test. Do not use aids to memory. The test should be completed in a single sitting.

The answers are on page 125.

1. CENOTAPH		box tomb pile
2. CRECHE		day night clerk
3. ANNUITY		axe sum mail
4. ARBOREAL		tree sail nil
5. BESOT		glass drink tea
6. CANT		slant flat first
7. COALESCE		tilt fly fuse
8. CONTRALTO		come buy singing
9. CONNUBIAL		marriage birth death
10. CLARION		type call fill
11. CLEMENCY		lenient prince tube
12. BELATED		dark before some
13. BENEDICK		son sun married
14. AFFIANCE		marriage pair pick
15. ANTITHETICAL		same opposite none
16. APOTHECARY		pharmacy cure case
17. BEDOUIN		boat base arab
18. BARD		singer play tree

19. APLOMB	corner name	confidence
20. APHORISM	nine maxim	street
21. ABJURE	tell renounce	take
22. ABROGATE	will annul	whisper
23. CAVIL	object teach	twist
24. CANONICAL	law wall	witch
25. ABNEGATE	reach feel	deny
26. ALACRITY	brisk stop	farming
27. AMULET	sing charm	glasses
28. ANGLOPHILE	USA USSR	UK
29. APPELLATION	title crown	crop
30. BACCHUS	grapes wine	fire
31. BEATITUDE	we Christ	God
32. BOVINE	ox cow	hen
33. CHAGRIN	disappointment doctor	fit
34. COHORT	tie companion	plant
35. CONCOMITANT	accompany search	plead
36. CONVOCATION	body floor	water
37. ACRIMONY	lecture boor	abuse
38. AMBIT	bitter precincts	better
39. ANODYNE	pain thirst	thrust
40. APOSTASY	faith church	minister
41. APPROBATION	praise raise	help
42. BALMY	silk soap	soothing
43. BANSHEE	grave death	life
44. BANTER	witty speech	bush
45. BAROQUE	desk dictionary	art
46. BATHOS	signature levity	climax
47. BEATIFIC	love hate	happy
48. BURGEON	heap blossom	steal
49. CARREL	library surface	stone
50. CHORTLE	cheat chase	chuckle
51. CONCERTO	solo ship	cheap
52. CUMMERBUND	sash slash	slight
53. CONSUMMATE	damage perfect	change
54. ALEATORY	money dice	change
55. ANTHROPOMORPHIC	effect sear	human
56. APOCRYPHAL	exact spurious	same
57. APOTHEOSIS	deify raise	fling
58. AQUILINE	bird eagle	nest

59. AVUNCULAR	aunty uncle father
60. BALEFUL	pernicious loving so
61. CARRION	stone earth flesh
62. CATECHISM	bible books questions
63. CATHARSIS	pure bushel language
64. CHARISMA	love prince lands
65. CHIMERA	cloud clown horror
66. CONCENTRATION	link join application
67. CONTAGION	partness contact no
68. ACRONYM	letters pens papers
69. ACROSTIC	label bail verse
70. ACEPHALOUS	headless body language
71. AEGIS	protocol protection wean
72. ADUMBRATE	sketch picture ketch
73. APHASIA	whine talk wine
74. ARCANE	mysterious plain common
75. ARGOT	cloth police dialect
76. ATAVISM	throwback face eye
77. BIBULOUS	coffee sugar drink
78. BIFURCATE	divorce divide rule
79. CALLOW	woman colour immature
80. CALUMNY	malicious cowardly worldly
81. CARMAGNOLE	German French Italian
82. CEPHALIC	toe finger head
83. BONHOMIE	kind Dick kid
84. CACHINNATION	laugh bat cave
85. BURLESQUE	idiot imitation cream
86. CHURL	gate lateness stingy
87. CINCTURE	belt state county
88. CLANDESTINE	judge firm secrecy
89. CODA	end beginning trust
90. COGNOMEN	child sister family
91. CONDUIT	dream pipe pill
92. CONTERMINOUS	
	common uncommon extraordinary
93. CONTIGUOUS	fare near soon
94. AVOCATION	tip top distraction
95. CONTRITION	sin sorrow sentence
96. ACHATES	me you friend
97. ANNOTATE	list note notes

98. ANTEDILUVIAN	arch seed flood
99. ASSUAGE	sweet pie pea
100. BARRANCA	hill gully gallery
101. BUNTING	strings fare flags
102. CANKER	sickness crabbed struck
103. CHILIASM	10 100 1,000
104. CHOLERIC	hear ear ire
105. ATRABILIOUS	silly angry peevish
106. AVERMENT	verify reify stupefy
107. ACME	basket journal summit
108. AGORAPHOBIA	time space journey
109. ALLEGORY	spirit soil spade
110. AMBIENCE	place stage sea
111. ANATHEMA	place curse lens
112. CORRIGENDUM	error lapsed erratum
113. CONDONATION	parole prison pardon
114. BULIMIA	drink food knife
115. BOSKY	woods wooden cut
116. CORYPHAEUS	leader follower flock
117. CHICANERY	show part trick
118. ANOMIE	conduct attention surrounds
119. ANDANTE	calmly slowly quickly
120. APROPOS	unimportant pertinent pointless
121. APERCUS	compendium stake thrill
122. APPANAGE	falsehood price adjunct
123. CHERUB	woman child grandmother
124. COELACANTH	fish bird plant
125. AMORTIZATION	postman mortmain pain
126. ANEURYSM	port vessel pots
127. CORUSCATE	collide sprinkle sparkle
128. ANISOTROPIC	axle axes axe
129. ANOSMIA	nose urine smell
130. CURVET	hoarse horse whore
131. AMANUENSIS	copyist lady waitress
132. AMBROSIA	drink food sour
133. CONTUMACY	court coarse course
134. ANIMALCULE	bird fish animal
135. ANABIOSIS	wakeful mindful sleep
136. ANASTROPHE	affectation effect fear

Answers

Test 1

1. 24; **2.** motto, maxim; **3.** cloth; **4.** chaos;
5. 1; **6.** bronze; **7.** animals; **8.** dulcet;
9. resign, stay; **10.** 39; **11.** expose;
12. black; **13.** retreat, haven; **14.** 38;
15. index; **16.** sombre, bright; **17.** acronym;
18. tycoon; **19.** 80; **20.** 3 minutes;
21. entertainment; **22.** relish, zest;
23. angry; **24.** spoken; **25.** protection;
26. £36; **27.** specification; **28.** grave,
facetious; **29.** sound; **30.** 7p

12-15	Average
16-21	Good
22-27	Very good
28-30	Exceptional

Test 2

1. B; **2.** E; **3.** B; **4.** C; **5.** A; **6.** D; **7.** C;
8. D; **9.** B; **10.** A

4-5	Average
6-7	Good
8-9	Very good
10	Exceptional

Note: These tests have been specially
compiled for this book, so an actual IQ rating
cannot be given.

Test 3

1. tomb; 2. day; 3. sum; 4. tree; 5. drink; 6. slant;
7. fuse; 8. singing; 9. marriage; 10. call; 11. lenient;
12. dark; 13. married; 14. marriage; 15. opposite;
16. pharmacy; 17. arab; 18. singer; 19. confidence;
20. maxim; 21. renounce; 22. annul; 23. object;
24. law; 25. deny; 26. brisk; 27. charm; 28. UK;
29. title; 30. wine; 31. Christ; 32. ox;
33. disappointment; 34. companion; 35. accompany;
36. body; 37. abuse; 38. precincts; 39. pain; 40. faith;
41. praise; 42. soothing; 43. death; 44. witty; 45. art;
46. climax; 47. happy; 48. blossom; 49. library;
50. chuckle; 51. solo; 52. sash; 53. perfect; 54. dice;
55. human; 56. spurious; 57. deify; 58. eagle;
59. uncle; 60. pernicious; 61. flesh; 62. questions;
63. pure; 64. love; 65. horror; 66. application;
67. contact; 68. letters; 69. verse; 70. headless;
71. protection; 72. sketch; 73. talk; 74. mysterious;
75. dialect; 76. throwback; 77. drink; 78. divide;
79. immature; 80. malicious; 81. French; 82. head;
83. kind; 84. laugh; 85. imitation; 86. stingy; 87. belt;
88. secrecy; 89. end; 90. family; 91. pipe;
92. common; 93. near; 94. distraction; 95. sorrow;
96. friend; 97. notes; 98. flood; 99. sweet; 100. gully;
101. flags; 102. crabbed; 103. 1,000; 104. ire;
105. peevish; 106. verify; 107. summit; 108. space;
109. spirit; 110. place; 111. curse; 112. erratum;
113. pardon; 114. food; 115. woods; 116. leader;
117. trick; 118. conduct; 119. slowly; 120. pertinent;
121. compendium; 122. adjunct; 123. child; 124. fish;
125. mortmain; 126. vessel; 127. sparkle; 128. axes;
129. smell; 130. horse; 131. copyist; 132. food;
133. court; 134. animal; 135. sleep; 136. effect

See page 126 for assessment rating for
Test 3.

The table is for the general adult population only
(Source: I.S.P.E. Selection)

With 61 correct – top	55% of the population	⎫
64	50	⎬ average
66	45	⎭
69	40	
71	35	
74	30	
76	25	
79	20	
81	15	
84	12	
86	10	
87	8	
89	7	
90	6	
92	5	
94	4	
96	3	
98	2	
102	1	
103	0.9	
104	0.8	
105	0.7	
106	0.6	
107	0.5	
108	0.4	
109	0.3	
111	0.2	
117	0.1	
119	0.07	
121	0.04	
123	0.03	
124	0.023	
125	0.013	
126	0.008	
127	0.007	
128	0.005	
129	0.003	
131	0.002	
134	0.001	
136	0.0004	

High-IQ Societies

General note: the data included here were correct at the time of writing, but are subject to change. In particular, the addresses of the smaller (more restrictive) societies may no longer be valid. In case of doubt, it may be helpful to consult the most recent edition of *The Encyclopedia of Associations* or some similar publication, or contact your local library.

Mensa (One in 50), founded in 1946 by Dr L. L. Ware. Journal: *Mensa International Journal* and several others.

Mensa is undoubtedly the best known of the High-IQ Societies that are active today; it is also the oldest and the one with the most members (some 100,000 worldwide). There are many Special Interest Groups or SIGs, including Humour SIG, Enigma SIG (for puzzle lovers), Cat SIG, Singles SIG and SIGHT, the SIG that provides Hospitality to Travellers (visiting Mensans from abroad) and often forges long-lasting friendships in the process.

British Mensa Ltd
Mensa House
St John's Square
Wolverhampton WV2 4AH

or

Mensa International Ltd
15 The Ivories,
6-8 Northampton Street
Islington
London N1 2HY

Intertel (One in 100), founded in 1966 by Ralph Haines. Journal: *Integra*.

Lourie Bill Davis
P.O. Box 1083
Tulsa
OK 74101
USA

Top One Percent Society (One in 100), founded in 1989 by Ron Hoeflin. Journal: *In-Genius*.

Ronald K. Hoeflin
PO Box 7430
New York
NY 10116
USA

I.S.P.E. (One in 1,000), founded in 1974 by Chris Harding. Journal: *Telicom*. When Chris Harding founded the International Society for Philosophical Enquiry, he wanted its members to make significant contributions to society in general. People join as Associates, on the basis of their potential; thereafter, they can attain the level of Member, Fellow, Senior Fellow, Senior Research Fellow and Diplomate through ongoing achievements.

Harry L. Callahan
P.O. Box 34304
Omaha
NE 68134
USA

Triple Nine Society
(One in 1,000), founded in 1979 by Richard Canty, Ron Hoeflin, Ronald Penner and Edward van Vleck. Journal *Vidya*.

PO Box 711
Excelsior
MN 55331
USA

Prometheus Society
(One in 30,000), founded in 1982 by Ron Hoeflin. Journal: *Nous*.
Robert Dick
13 Speer Street
Somerville
NJ 08876
USA

Mega Society
(One in 1,000,000), founded in 1982 by Ron Hoeflin. Journal: *Noesis*.

According to the *Guinness Book of World Records*, the Mega Society is the most exclusive of today's High-IQ Societies; there are only about two dozen members.

Jeff Ward
13155 Wimberly Sq. #284
San Diego
CA 92128
USA